MIRACLE AT FATIMA

MIRACLE AT FATIMA

BY

WILHELM HUNERMANN

TRANSLATED FROM THE GERMAN
BY ISABEL AND FLORENCE McHUGH

P. J. KENEDY & SONS
NEW YORK

MIRACLE AT FATIMA
is a translation of *Der Himmel Ist Stärker Als Wir*
by Wilhelm Hunermann—Mainz, *Mattias-Grünewald-Verlag*,
1956

Nihil obstat: DANIEL V. FLYNN, J.C.D.
Censor Librorum

Imprimatur: ✠ FRANCIS CARDINAL SPELLMAN

New York
September 15, 1959

The nihil obstat and imprimatur are official declarations that a book or pamphlet is free of doctrinal or moral error. No implication is contained therein that those who have granted the nihil obstat and imprimatur agree with the contents, opinions or statements expressed.

Library of Congress Catalog Card Number: 59-13900
Copyright © 1959 by P. J. Kenedy & Sons, New York

CONTENTS

FOREWORD

The pale gold of the wintry sunshine slanted down on the gentle hills of the Serra de Aire, and the olive, fir and fig trees lay dreaming under a clear blue sky.

Once more I wandered away from the mighty white Basilica which stands enthroned above the Cova da Iria and sought the silent moorland of Valinhos. A few sheep and goats grazed among the crags of the Cabeço; a shepherd boy was playing a melancholy melody on his flute. Otherwise all was silent and solitary.

So this countryside had been the scene of those astounding celestial wonders: the golden globe of light that moved across the sky; the rain of blossoms; the dance of the sun. Over this remote region heaven had opened up; the Virgin Mary had appeared amid a flutter of angels' wings, and had spoken to three shepherd children in the familiar dialect of their mountain homeland.

A peasant woman with eyes inflamed from the constant smoke of her kitchen fire was climbing up the hill toward me, a flaxen-haired grandchild on her arm. She told me she was a cousin of the little seers, and showed herself most willing to talk about these relatives of hers who had been so marvelously favored by heaven.

"Lucia? Oh, yes! She was a pious, serious child. And what a lot she had to suffer because nobody believed her, not even her mother.

"Jacinta? A sweet, merry, wild little creature she was! And how she loved to dance! Why, even in the prison she went spinning round in a fandango. But, my! What strength of mind she had for sacrifice and suffering! *O meu Deus!* What a child!

"Francisco? The little minstrel of Valinhos he was. And he loved all animals so much, just like his holy patron!"

Before one of the big boulders on the Cabeço the woman remained standing, kissed it solemnly, then made the sign of the cross on her grandchild's forehead.

"It was here the angel appeared to them," she whispered as if we were in church. Then, fearing I would ask about the heavenly happenings, she looked at me with widened eyes and said: "*Não se pode falar destas coisas. São coisas de cima!*" (One cannot talk about these things. They are things from above).

Oh, yes, don't I know it! There are no words for them. Any word seems a desecration of the wonder. To try to describe it is like taking a delicate flower in one's hands— its bloom is destroyed.

When Lucia was shown the picture of Our Lady which a young artist had painted strictly in accordance with her own description, she shook her head and said:

"She was like that, and yet she was not. She was Light, Light, Light!"

Many years later in her silent convent cell, after she had written down her account of the visions, she felt dreadfully unhappy because of her failure to describe the indescribable. The happenings in Fatima come within the domain of the inaccessible light of heaven.

Now, even though I have written this book, I have been fully conscious all the time of the impossibility of expressing the ineffable. Yet I trust all the same, dear Reader, that it may succeed in conveying to your soul some idea of the miracle of grace that took place for all of us under the golden sun of Portugal.   THE AUTHOR

PROLOGUE

Luis, the village piper of Fatima, was wandering along the stony Valinhos road, merrily playing on his flute. It was springtime, and the olive trees were a silvery shimmer of bloom. Bees and butterflies buzzed and fluttered over the white blossoms; the birds were singing their morning song in the branches of the olive and fig trees, the firs and the evergreen oaks. In the distance the sailcloth wings of the windmills were turning in glistening circles. The perfume-laden air was filled with sunshine and the harmonious music of nature.

Grand weather for vagabonds, thought the wandering musician. Just right for roaming through the world and stealing a day's sunshine from the good God!

The musician was a queer bird—roamer, poet, philosopher and ne'er-do-well all rolled into one. Every day was Sunday for him, and he avoided work like the plague. Why should he worry, anyway? He always got his bite to eat one way or another, and took his seat as though by right at the festive board of life whether anyone invited him or not. When he played at village festivals and weddings nobody begrudged him a place, for he always had a merry joke on his lips.

For nine months of the year the sun warmed his limbs, and there was always plenty of wood to give him a little fire for the few winter months. Oranges, figs, olives and grapes simply pushed their way into his mouth, so to speak, and now and then a fowl found its way into his pot.

He had been roaming about the world for years and years. He knew every road in Portugal and Spain and far beyond, yet he had never spent a centavo on shoe leather. The soles on which he walked had been made for him by the good God. And the splendid thing about them was that they grew harder and firmer the more he walked on them. Now and then a policeman grabbed him by the collar. This meant free board and lodging for a couple of weeks behind iron bars. But this only happened when autumn, like a musician clad in motley, had departed and given place to winter with its dark, depressing mantle of mist and rain.

"Hello, Luis!" the piper heard as he began toiling up the rocky path to Cabeço Hill. A little, barefooted, six-year-old girl, with chestnut-brown hair and eyes as dark as blackberries, ran toward him and flung herself into his arms laughing merrily.

"Jacinta!" cried the man, lifting her up and swinging her round in a circle. "Well, you *did* give me a fright!"

"Ah, you weren't that frightened!" laughed the child. "Come and play for us. We want to dance!"

"Yes, do sit down and tell us a story," came a boy's clear voice, "but a true story, not made up like most of the ones you tell us!" demanded Francisco, the son of Farmer Marto of Aljustrel, who was two years older than his little sister Jacinta. The village piper looked kindly at the small boy with his fresh sunburned cheeks who jumped out from among the rocks, his shepherd's staff in his hand.

"Made up stories, indeed!" said the piper gruffly. "Old Luis always tells the real truth, and if the facts don't always square with it, well, all the more pity for the facts!"

"That's too learned for me; I don't understand it," said Francisco, shaking his dark tousled head. "When I tell a lie, Father gives me a good hiding!"

"You're not a poet like me," said Luis, laughing. "That's why!"

"Are you a poet?" asked the boy, staring at him wonderstruck.

"Are poets allowed to tell lies?" asked Jacinta, equally mystified.

"You don't understand these things, you impertinent imps," said the piper, sitting down on a boulder and stretching out his legs in the warm sunshine. "Poets live in another world that they make for themselves. It's a real world for them, and for those who believe them, too."

"They must be funny people!" said Francisco pensively. "But do begin the story!"

"Hello, you two!" cried a little girl of about nine who came climbing up through the rocks from the pastures. "You're nice shepherds indeed!" she cried, pushing her black hair away from her perspiring forehead. "Chatting here and not caring a fig whether or not the wolves come and eat our sheep!"

"There are no wolves in Valinhos!" said the boy, yawning. "Nothing will eat our sheep, and neither can they do any harm here."

"See who's here, Lucia!" cried Jacinta eagerly.

"Oh, the piper!" exclaimed her cousin joyfully. "Play us a *vira* or a fandango and we'll dance!"

"No, tell us a story," pleaded the boy once more.

"Very well, a story first and then the fandango," said the piper. He thought for a few moments, smiling to himself. Then he began: "As you know, Francisco, I was in the 6th Infantry Battalion with your father in Leiria. He was a brave soldier, your father was. Soon after that we set sail for Africa to fight a rebel chief named Gungunnana. The savages were a cunning lot; they lay in ambush for us in the great forests and shot at us with poisoned arrows. Many a brave Portuguese gave his last gasp there and was eaten up by the lions."

"By the lions?" exclaimed Jacinta horrified.

"Of course! They were running about the bush by the dozens. One day, as I was lying in front of my tent having my midday nap, two of the beasts came running up to me, howling most terribly. One came from the left, the other from the right. It was hard to know what to do. I hadn't even a gun with me. So I jumped up and stood right between the two lions. They both made a leap at the same time to get at my throat."

"And then?" asked Jacinta with feverish excitement.

"With that I ducked down, and the heads of the two lions collided one against the other with such force that the animals fell to the ground unconscious."

"And then?"

"Then I tied them together by the tails so that they could not run away, fetched my gun, and shot the two of them dead."

"Ah, you told us that one before," grumbled the boy. "I asked Father if it were true and he said you hadn't seen any lions at all, any of you. You only had heard them roaring in the distance sometimes. But he said there were lots of monkeys there, and crocodiles, too."

"Well, if you don't believe me, I'll go!" said Luis standing up and pretending to be offended.

"Don't go! Please sit down again!" begged Francisco. "Perhaps you really did see lions sometimes."

"Very well, then."

"Tell us something else!" begged Lucia. "But it must be true. I don't like lies."

"Now then, listen!" said the piper, giving in. "More than a thousand years ago the Moors came over from Africa and conquered all of Spain and Portugal. They were unbelievers and worshipped Allah and Mohammed his Prophet, instead of Christ and the Blessed Virgin."

"That's true! Mother told me that, too!" agreed Lucia.

"The Portuguese knights won back parts of the country from them bit by bit, and a Christian king set up his war camp in Santarém. One day—it was the feast of St. John —a company of noble Moorish knights riding magnificent horses, and aristocratic Moorish ladies in gilded litters, came down from the Alcácer do Sal to the Sado River. Suddenly a troop of Portuguese knights came galloping down on them, sparks flying from their horses' hoofs. Their leader was Dom Goncalo Hermingues, who was known as 'the Scourge of the Moors.' There was a desperate fight and many of the Moors were killed. The Moorish knights who were not killed and the ladies were brought to the King at Santarém."

"And what happened then?" asked Jacinta when Luis paused.

"The King was delighted with the successful raid and he told 'the Scourge of the Moors' that he could ask for any favor he wished. Now, among the Moorish ladies there was a princess. She was as beautiful as a day in May. Dom Goncalo asked the King for the hand of Fatima—for that was the name of the princess. The noble lady Fatima liked the brave knight, so she married him and became a Christian. When she was baptized she took the name of Oureana. The King gave 'the Scourge of the Moors' the little town of Abdegas as a wedding present, and from then onward it was called Oureana after the princess. Today its name is Ourém."

"Oh, yes, I know. Ourém is three hours' walk from here," put in Francisco.

"Many years passed by," the piper continued. "Then the beautiful Moorish princess died. Goncalo was so grieved at her death that he put on a monk's habit and founded a monastery near Ourém. There he buried his wife, and he called the place Fatima. So now you know how your native village got its name."

"That was a lovely story," said Francisco, "and perhaps it's true, though a person never really knows with your stories."

"Oho! You're more unbelieving than the worst Turks and Moors!"

"Now let's dance!" pleaded Jacinta.

The musician did not have to be asked twice. He took up his flute and soon the girls were dancing the fandango, whirling round and round and snapping their fingers as they had seen the dancers doing on the church square in Fatima. Francisco marked time by clapping his hands.

"Now I must be going," said Luis when the song was finished.

"Oh, is it over already?" asked Jacinta, disappointed.

"Don't mind; I can play for your dancing, too," said the boy, taking out a little flute he had carved from a sugar cane. Then, as Luis walked away laughing, Francisco struck up a merry tune, and the little girls danced until they were dead tired. Meantime, it was getting toward midday, and the sun was moving over the heights of the Serra de Aire.

"Let's eat!" suggested Francisco, opening the cloth bag into which their mother had put their bread and cheese.

"We still have to say the rosary," Lucia reminded him.

"Yes, but the short one," said Jacinta. The short rosary was her own invention, and it was very simple. You simply said the two words "Our Father" on the big beads and "Hail Mary" on the others, nothing more. That kind of rosary was over quickly. It hardly took two minutes.

"Very well," said Francisco. "I agree to the short rosary."

The blessed beads slipped quickly through their fingers and soon they made the final sign of the cross.

"Let's eat now!" urged the boy. "I'm hungry as a wolf."

So they bit into the hard corn bread. Out here in the fresh air it tasted specially good. When the meal was over Jacinta's eyes fell on the rosary beads lying on the grass beside her. Taking them thoughtfully in her hands, she looked at the crucifix.

"Why is Our Saviour nailed on?" she asked Lucia.

"Because He died for us."

"Tell us about it!" And sitting in the radiant sunshine of Valinhos the nine-year-old girl told her little cousins of the bitter sufferings and death of Jesus.

"Why did He suffer so much?" asked Jacinta.

"Because He wanted to atone for people's sins," explained Lucia, who had made her First Holy Communion three years before and knew all these things by heart.

"Then I'll try not to commit any more sins," said Jacinta, sighing. Looking at the crucifix once more, she said sadly, "Our poor Saviour!"

"That was a long time ago and it doesn't hurt Him any more now," said Francisco to console her. But Lucia explained to him that even now the Saviour suffers for every sin which is committed anywhere in the world, and that anyone who commits a mortal sin nails Jesus to the cross anew.

"A mortal sin? But who would commit a mortal sin?" asked Francisco.

"Oh, there are many mortal sins committed every day in the world, that's certain," said Lucia. "And that is why there is so much suffering and unhappiness, especially now when there's war and so many soldiers have to die. If only there was peace again!"

"A whole lot of men from Fatima have joined up as soldiers, too, and perhaps they will even have to go to the war. José das Neves' son went off to the barracks in Leiria yesterday."

"We really ought to say another rosary for the soldiers and for peace," said Lucia.

"It would be nicer to sing a hymn," suggested Jacinta. Without waiting for an answer, she began to sing in a high clear voice, the other two children joining in:

> "I adore the Lord in heaven above,
> I love Him below on this earth so drear.
> The fields, the flowers and the stars I love,
> And to me all the sheep of my flock are dear.
>
> "I frolic about with my gentle sheep
> With a joyful heart, in the midday glow,
> And sing to the tinkle of distant bells
> Which rises from verdant vales below.
>
> "I am only a shepherd, humble and poor,
> Watching alone on the vast prairie,

But in the glow of the sunshine pure,
My heart gladly greets my Mother Mary!

"O aye! O aye!
May I but see Thee one day, O Jesus,
O aye! O aye!
On the sunlit heavenly pastures."

The sweet melody of the old Portuguese shepherds' hymn floated joyfully over the flowery hillside. Suddenly the children jumped up in alarm. A fierce gust of wind was sweeping down from the mountains. Then they saw something coming toward them across the silvery-green and white of the flowering olive trees—something luminous and beautiful, whiter than snow, and more brilliant than glass when the sun shines on it. The dazzling white assumed a form, the form of a young man in a radiant white garment. He now stood before the children, who were able to look at him face to face. They stared terrified at the strange messenger. Then he spoke, and his voice had a wonderful silvery tone.

"Do not be afraid," he said. "I am the Angel of Peace. Clasp your hands and pray with me."

Trembling, the little shepherds fell on their knees. The angel knelt down, too, touched his face to the ground, and recited three times the same prayer:

"My God, I believe, I adore, I hope, I love You. I ask pardon for those who do not believe, nor adore, nor hope in You, nor love You!"

When the angel began the prayer for the third time, the two little girls repeated the words after him, and Francisco, who had not heard the heavenly voice, on hearing the other children praying with such fervor, felt overcome with awe, and shuddered.

The angel stood up and said, "That is how you should pray. The holy Hearts of Jesus and Mary will listen to your petitions." Then he disappeared from their sight.

For a long time the little ones remained kneeling, numb with surprise. At last they stood up. Was what they had seen real? They looked around them bewildered. Were they still really with their sheep on the hillside of Valinhos? Everything was as before. Nothing had changed. They saw the olive trees in full bloom, the butterflies fluttering from blossom to blossom, the sheep grazing peacefully on the slopes.

"I think I have been dreaming," stammered Jacinta, rubbing her eyes. "Ah, what a lovely, lovely dream it was! I saw an angel!"

"So did I," said Francisco. "I saw him, too, but I didn't hear anything."

"It wasn't a dream," said Lucia quietly. "We couldn't all three have had the same dream. Besides, we weren't sleeping, we were singing. Don't you remember?"

"Yes, we were singing, and then that heavenly being came," said the little boy thoughtfully.

"He called himself the Angel of Peace," Jacinta reminded Lucia. "That means there will soon be peace!"

"I simply can't understand it," said Francisco, shaking his head. "When have shepherds ever before seen an angel?"

"When Our Lord was born," replied Lucia, "an angel appeared to the shepherds in Bethlehem and said exactly the same words to them: 'Don't be afraid!' He too brought news of peace."

"Yes, you're right," said the boy, "but that was more than a thousand years ago, in a country far, far away, and in the night, not in Valinhos right in the middle of the day."

"I still think it was a dream, but it was a very lovely dream," insisted Jacinta.

The children were so wrapped up in their thoughts that, after Lucia had told Francisco what the angel had said, they did not speak a word to each other until evening, when they drove home their sheep. Back in Aljustrel, they felt as though they had returned from a strange and distant world. Yet in the little hamlet everything was exactly as before. There was old Rosa carrying her flat basket of fish on her head as she did every day; and the sullen old cobbler Farzeria panting along the road with his hand on his back as usual because he was tormented with the gout. He was probably on his way to Guimarães' tavern, where he spent almost every centavo he earned. Only one girl, Luisa Bernardos, looked much sadder than usual today. That was probably because her sweetheart had had to go off to be a soldier. No, nothing at all had changed.

When the two Marto children came in after driving the sheep into the sheepfold, their mother was standing by the hearth cooking the supper as always.

"We saw something beautiful in Valinhos," began Jacinta, "but perhaps it was only a dream."

Her mother hardly listened to her. "Put the plates on the table," she ordered. "Your father and brothers and sisters will be in from the fields soon."

No, there was no opportunity to talk about it. And perhaps—perhaps after all it was only a dream.

Children's days are long; there is something of the timelessness of eternal life about them. And so the three little shepherds, playing on a hot day that summer under the chestnut and plum trees by the well of Farmer Antonio dos Santos, Lucia's father, had already almost forgotten about the strange apparition. Then all of a sudden the angel was there again! The beautiful messenger from heaven was standing beside them as if he had come from neighbor Das Neves' olive grove. All three children saw him, but only the little girls heard his voice.

"What are you doing?" he asked them. "Pray! The Hearts of Jesus and Mary have designs of mercy on you. Serve the Most High by prayer and sacrifice!"

"How shall we make sacrifices?" stammered Lucia, who thought of the priests' Holy Sacrifice at the altar.

"Pray and offer sacrifice continually to the Lord in reparation for the many sins which offend Him; and pray for the conversion of sinners! Then peace will come to your country. I am the Angel of Portugal!"

"How shall we make sacrifices?" asked Lucia again.

"Offer up everything as a sacrifice. Accept with submission the sufferings which it will please the Lord to send you, and bear them patiently."

And again the angel vanished from their sight.

"What did he say?" asked Francisco excitedly, when he had found his speech again.

"Didn't you hear him?" asked Jacinta.

"No, no! I didn't hear anything. I only saw—I only saw, just like that time in Valinhos. Do tell me what he said, Lucia!"

"I can't, I can't tell anything now," cried Lucia, still quite bewildered, and she walked away.

"Won't you tell me?" the boy begged his little sister. But Jacinta shook her head and went off, leaving her brother alone. She too was unable to utter a word.

The next morning, while they were minding their sheep on the Cabeço Hill, the girls finally told Francisco every word that the angel had spoken. He could not understand much of it, and again and again he asked what the words meant, but even Lucia could not explain them all to him.

Autumn came. The children spent one glorious day helping to pick the grapes in the little vineyard. After that they returned with their sheep to the old familiar pasturage. It was evening. The sun was sinking in a blaze of glory behind the Serra, leaving the whole sky lit up in red and gold behind it. On this occasion, near a little cave, the angel appeared to the children for the third time.

Bowing down to the ground he said, "Most Holy Trinity! I adore you from the depths of my soul! I offer you the Most Precious Body and Blood of Our Lord Jesus Christ present in all the tabernacles of the world, in reparation for all the outrages committed against Him; and by the infinite merits of His Sacred Heart, through the intercession of the Immaculate Heart of Mary, I pray for the conversion of poor sinners."

He repeated this prayer three times and then disappeared into the brilliant afterglow of the sunset.

As the children returned home the stars were already lighting up the sky.

"I love the angel," said Jacinta wistfully, "but I don't know why it is that I can't dance and sing any more. I can hardly even speak; I really don't know why it is."

And they walked home under the twinkling stars.

How could the children understand what had happened to them? They did not speak about it to anyone, and even Jacinta's voice failed her when she tried once or twice to tell her mother about it. She simply could not talk about it. It was just the same with the other two. It was an inexplicable and unutterable secret between heaven and these souls which had been touched by the grace of God.

Winter came. Storms and heavy rain swept over the countryside. At night the wind howled around the windows and wakened the children. Often, at such times, they thought of the strange things that they had experienced, and they whispered the prayers that the angel had taught them.

Spring came and the cold gave way to warm, sunny days. The olive trees began to bud and the world once more became full of light and sweet perfumes and the songs of birds. The quiet countryside, with its hills and mountains, was profoundly peaceful. But the war was not yet over. Many of Portugal's sons were fighting and dying for other countries, far from home.

One day in May, Farmer Marto's second son, Manuel, was called to the colors. Jacinta, who loved her big jolly brother with all her heart, cried the whole day before he went away.

"Don't fret, little sister," he said to her. "I may not have to go to the front at all. The war will surely be over long before I'm off!" And as her tears kept on flowing, he took his mouth organ out of his pocket and played a fandango. "Dance, little sister, dance!" he cried. "I know how you love dancing!"

The music succeeded where all words of comfort had failed. Jacinta wiped away her tears and whirled round, shouting merrily as she danced.

"I'll pray for you a whole lot on Sunday!" she promised, flinging herself into his arms. "I'll pray to your angel guardian, and I'll pray to another angel, too."

"Who's the other angel?" asked her brother, laughing.

"The Angel of Portugal," whispered the child, and she flushed with joy as she thought of him.

"I never knew that countries had angels, too," said Manuel.

"But I know; I know it for certain."

"If you pray for me I'll surely come home safely," said her brother, kissing the little girl.

❦ 1 ❧

A SUNDAY IN MAY

Morning dawned, and the olive trees, crowded together in groups over the wide stretch of hilly country, sleepily shook the night dew from their disheveled crowns and stretched their silvery branches into the golden sunshine. In the whitewashed cottages of Aljustrel, families were awakening, too. The shining windows were pushed open and people looked out into the morning that was becoming more sunny and glorious at every moment, as befitted a Sunday morning in May. The church bells of the little hamlet of Boleiros sang out their Gloria in unison with the chorus of thousands of birds, calling the faithful to the *Missa das almas*, the early Mass that was celebrated every Sunday for the souls in purgatory.

Dom Marcus Ferreira, the parish priest of Fatima, celebrated this early Mass in the various villages and hamlets of his parish in turn. But the High Mass was always celebrated in Fatima itself.

In Aljustrel, doors opened and young and old set out for church dressed in their Sunday best. And what crowds there were! Who could have believed that so many people could live in those tiny cottages? The Aljustrel folk had few worldly goods, but they had many children. These were God's richest gift to the village.

Olimpia Marto reviewed the small troop of children with which God had blessed her marriage, smoothed out a crease here and there on the girls' bodices, skirts or scarves, straightened the boys' peaked wool caps, and only then allowed the little crowd to leave the house. Their father, Manuel Pedro, looked on with an amused smile as he puffed at his clay pipe. He was full of jokes and in high spirits as always.

"Now let us drive our little flock to the heavenly sheepfold," he said with a twinkle in his eye to his wife, a tiny woman of dynamic energy and courage. "I think the good God must enjoy the sight of them, you've dressed them up so fine."

"Well, that is only as it should be when we go to God's house," she replied. But all the same she looked at the children with secret satisfaction as they set off, all spruce and clean, and with healthy sunburned faces.

The two eldest, the children of her first marriage, were not there. Antonio had married a short time before, and Manuel, of course, had gone into the barracks in Lisbon. If only he were not sent to the front!

That was in the year 1917. Many young lives were being sacrificed on the battlefields of France, and many a young man who had marched off healthy and merry returned home a cripple.

"May God protect Manuel!" prayed Olimpia. If the war went on much longer perhaps José, who was nineteen now, would be called, too. After him, thank God, there were two girls, Florinda and Teresa, and then João and Francisco, who were still young children. And finally there was seven-year-old Jacinta, the darling of them all and the pet of the house.

As they passed Farmer Santos' house, Maria-Rosa and her children came out and joined them. The families greeted each other warmly.

"Where's Antonio?" asked Manuel.

"He's going to the High Mass in Fatima," replied Maria-Rosa shortly. Ah, yes, her husband was a cause of great sorrow to her. He was certainly not a bad man, but in religious matters he was decidedly indifferent. He did not often miss Mass on Sunday, to be sure, but he had not received Holy Communion for many years, and the mother bore the sole responsibility for the religious upbringing of the children. Maria-Rosa was a silent, serious, deeply devout woman, and often in the evenings she taught her children the Catechism. Neighbors' children came to share the instruction, and no priest could have taught them better than she did.

"Where shall we take the sheep today?" Francisco asked Lucia, the youngest of the Santos children, as they all walked along together toward the church.

"We'll go to Gouveia," replied Lucia.

"That's grand. There's a lovely echo there," replied Jacinta merrily.

They had almost reached the tiny church when Dom Marcus caught up to them on his bicycle. The parish priest of Fatima was a serious and zealous priest, who tried to look after his flock well. His penetrating eyes, under their dark bushy brows, could look quite severe at times, and all the children felt great respect for him. So the boys quickly pulled off their caps and the girls dropped hurried curtsies.

"What a beautiful day!" cried the priest amiably.

"Yes, indeed, Father. It's wonderful weather," replied Manuel, beaming with contentment.

"Well, good-by," cried the parish priest, after this brief greeting, and rode on.

At last they arrived at the church. The women went straight in with the children, but Manuel lingered outside to finish his pipe and exchange a Sunday greeting with his neighbors. Most of them enjoyed a little chat before Mass on Sundays. Only José das Neves, who was leading his blind son, passed them by with a brief *"Bom dia!"*

My God, he has been hard hit, thought Manuel with deep pity. Two of his daughters died in the bloom of youth, and now his eldest son has come back from the war blinded.

Antonio Guimarães, the tavern keeper of Fatima, called out a friendly greeting to Manuel. He was rather stout, and, in spite of the early hour, was wiping the perspiration from his forehead. "It will be a hot day," he panted.

"All the better for you," said Marto, grinning. "People will be thirstier in the heat."

"I have a splendid Dão in just now," Antonio assured him eagerly. "You should try my wine some time. The angels in heaven don't drink anything better."

"Then you should invite them to try it one day. Perhaps they pay well!"

"You're an incorrigible buffoon," muttered Guimarães.

Farzeria, the cobbler, who was plagued with the gout in spite of the fine day, now joined the others. "Let's hope the parish priest makes his sermon short," he said glumly. "But today is the thirteenth. I'm always unlucky on the thirteenth. I'll wager the priest will go on and on."

"You'd be more comfortable in my place than in the church," advised the tavern keeper, eager for business.

"Come on! It's time to go in," said Manuel, knocking his pipe on the heel of his boot and then going into the church.

Dom Marcus Ferreira was a man with great powers of speech, and his sermons often resounded like thunder over the heads of his congregation. But this Sunday before the Feast of the Ascension he took out a sheet of paper and proceeded to read it.

The shoemaker Farzeria decided to have a nap. He liked pastoral letters because while reading them the priest could not notice so easily if someone nodded in front of the pulpit. But this time Farzeria's drowsiness was quickly dispelled. The parish priest read an Encyclical from Pope Benedict XV that was read in every Catholic church throughout the world on that day.

In it the Pope spoke of the horrors of the war, of the frightful bloodshed that showed no signs of coming to an end. Only hands raised in prayer could restore what hands raised to strike were destroying, he wrote. And the Holy Father went on to say that he placed all his trust in Our Lady, whom he called *"Regina Pace,"* Queen of Peace. Every Christian in the world should have recourse to her and implore her to intercede with God to bring an end to the horrors of war, he said.

Dom Marcus folded the Encyclical slowly and thoughtfully, then proceeded to speak from the depths of his heart: "Pray, my brethren, pray without ceasing to our dear Lady, to whom the parish of Fatima is specially dedicated. Say the rosary devoutly every day. It is the weapon with which Portugal defended herself against the infidel who occupied our country many hundreds of years ago. As your parish priest, I implore you all to say the rosary.

For enough blood has been shed, and it is time that God should free us from this heavy affliction."

The priest looked down sadly on the congregation. He knew of the grief that had come to many homes. He saw weeping mothers who would never see their sons again. He saw the blind man, the son of José das Neves, whose sightless eyes were raised to the pulpit; and Ricardo, the poor cripple with his mutilated legs, whose mother pushed him to church every Sunday in a little cart. And he saw the most unfortunate of them all, poor Luisa Bernardos. Her sweetheart had fallen in France before they had had time to be married, and now she had a baby who was without a father. The youths of Fatima pointed the finger of scorn at the poor girl, for she was the only one in the village, for many years now, who had had an illegitimate child. Luisa kept her head bowed under her black kerchief and did not dare look up. True, her sin had been great, but the parish priest felt very sorry for her, and he thought of Our Lord's words: "He that is without sin among you, let him first cast a stone at her."

More than once Dom Marcus had come to her rescue and chased away the boys who were jeering and throwing dirt at her. He prayed that God might help the poor girl and give her courage to bear her misfortune.

"Pray, my dear brethren!" cried the priest once more. "Pray that God may be merciful to us and that our dear Mother Mary may take us to her heart! Amen."

After Mass the people remained kneeling in front of the picture of Our Lady of Good Counsel, before which they lighted candles. Each one had some trouble of body or soul, and, as they lighted the candles, they prayed for help and comfort.

Lucia too was drawn as if by some mysterious force to the picture of the Blessed Virgin, and a silent prayer went out from her heart. Lucia's family had left the church long ago, but the little girl lingered on, gazing devoutly at the picture. When she stood up at last she was alone except for one person who was kneeling motionless, her head bowed down almost to the ground. It was poor Luisa, who did not even dare to look up at the picture of Our Lady.

Lucia hesitated for a moment as she passed her. She too knew that the boys of the village jeered and shouted nasty things after her, though she did not understand what they meant. She knew that the girls said wicked things about Luisa when they went to the well to fill their earthenware pitchers. Of course the unhappy girl was guilty of some terrible thing that Lucia did not quite understand, but she suddenly felt a great pity in her heart for the poor outlawed creature.

"I will pray for her," she promised herself as she dipped her fingers in the holy water font and left the church.

❧ 2 ❧

THE BEAUTIFUL LADY

An hour later the three children set out for Gouveia with their flock. Jacinta was carrying a lamb on her shoulder. She loved all her sheep and had a name for each one of them, but she loved the little lamb most of all.

"Let the lamb run along by itself," said Francisco. "You will be tired before we get to Gouveia."

"Snowflake will be tired, too," said the little girl, shaking her head. "You know she's still very young."

"Mother put something special into our tuck bag today—a big piece of cheese," her brother told her. "We'll have a good meal!"

"You're always thinking about things to eat," said Lucia, laughing.

"Yes, and my godfather Uncle Francisco gave me a present of twenty centavos. We can buy some cakes at old Christina's when we're passing her shop."

"Oh, that will be lovely," cried Jacinta, for she too liked nice things to eat.

Francisco took his flute out of his pocket and began to play a lively tune as they walked along.

Suddenly Lucia stopped. "I've been thinking we should drive the sheep to the Cova da Iria," she said.

"But that's in exactly the opposite direction!" replied Francisco very much surprised.

Lucia could not have explained why she wanted to go somewhere else. She simply felt that she must go to the valley of Iria today. "It's too far to go to Gouveia today," she offered at last. "We must be home in good time for the May devotions."

"I don't mind," said Francisco, but Jacinta sulked for a while because she loved the echoes that could be heard from the mountains in Gouveia. But she followed the others without any protest.

When they reached Aljustrel, they met Luis, the village piper. "Home already from the pastures?" he laughed, surprised. "So you've only taken your sheep for a short Sunday stroll, eh?"

"We want to go to the Cova da Iria," explained Jacinta, who liked the merry fellow although he spent more time in the taverns than in church.

"Aha! So you lost your way? Well, your legs have to pay for your mistake. Fine shepherds indeed!" continued Luis.

Francisco, whose pride was hurt, replied crossly: "Well, they're our sheep, and we may drive them anywhere we like!"

"Oho! You needn't be so touchy!" said the roguish fellow. "And by the way, Francisco, I've an old flute for you at home; you'll be able to get much better music out of it than from that sugar cane of yours. You can come and fetch it this evening."

"Oh, thank you!" cried the boy, beaming, his anger quite forgotten.

"Perhaps you'll be a village piper one day," said Luis, laughing.

Francisco shook his head. "No, I'm going to be a farmer like Father," he replied.

As they were leaving the village, they met some boys who had caught a goldfinch. Francisco, who, like his patron St. Francis, loved all birds and could not bear to see any bird or animal suffering, shouted angrily at them: "What are you doing to the poor goldfinch? Don't you see how frightened it is?"

"What should we do with it?" replied one of the boys. "We'll probably put it in a cage and make it sing."

"Or we might roast it and eat it," said another.

Francisco wondered whether he should free the captive bird by force. He did not mind an honest fight, but one against four—that would be a bit too much! The chance of winning was too slender, so he decided to try bargaining instead.

"Will you sell me the goldfinch?"

"How much will you give us for it?"

"I've twenty centavos."

"Let's see them!"

Francisco fished them out of his breeches pocket.

"Very well, if you're so silly as to give all that money for a bird, here it is."

The money and the goldfinch changed hands, and Francisco felt the tiny heart beating violently as he held the bird. Then he cautiously loosened his fingers and let the frightened creature go free. "Take care not to be caught again!" he called after it as it flew away.

"It's easy to see what a fool you are!" the boys jeered as he left them, but Francisco did not mind. He started to play his sugar-cane flute once more, and all the birds in the oak trees and olive trees along the way joined in the music.

"There go our cakes flying away!" said Jacinta with a sigh as she looked after the goldfinch.

"Ah, what do cakes matter? And anyway we're not passing by old Christina's shop after all."

The three children continued on their way in silence. Their eyes wandered over the extensive landscape—the stony, reddish-brown earth which yielded but poor pasture, the miserable little patches of tillage surrounded by limestone walls, the olive trees and the stunted oak trees that rose from the ground in fantastic shapes. Nevertheless, the countryside seemed to them wonderfully beautiful, for it was filled with radiant sunshine right to the edge of the distant blue mountains.

At last the children arrived at the Cova da Iria, a large hollow dotted with evergreen oak. The Santos' owned a stretch of land here where the children now turned in the sheep to graze. Jacinta was fairly tired, for she had carried her lamb all the long way. With a sigh and a caress, she put it down but was very careful to see that neither the lamb nor any of the other sheep damaged the nearby gardens. The children had been brought up to respect other people's property strictly.

"Play for us, Francisco," suggested Jacinta when they had rested for a while. Her brother did not need to be asked twice, and he began to pipe a lively tune. Jacinta jumped up and started to dance. Her feet moved so gracefully in time with the music, her full skirt whirled round so rapidly, and she snapped her fingers so nimbly and cleverly that it was a delight to look at her.

"Do come and dance with me, Lucia!" she called out joyously to her cousin. At other times Lucia would have jumped up at once, for she too loved dancing, as did all the girls of Fatima. But this time she shook her head.

"No, I don't want to," she said. "Don't you remember what the priest said this morning: it isn't a time for dancing, but for praying! Stop playing, Francisco. We haven't said the rosary yet today."

"Oh, must we stop already?" asked the little girl, pouting.

But after playing a few notes, the boy put away his flute and said, "All right, you say the rosary and I'll watch the sheep so they don't go into the peas."

"We can watch them while we're praying," said Lucia. "Have you forgotten already what the angel said to us?"

"He didn't say a word about reciting the rosary," laughed the little boy, and trotted off with his shepherd's staff.

Francisco had not forgotten the heavenly messenger, but he was not very fond of saying the rosary. While the girls were reciting the Glorious Mysteries loudly and solemnly in honor of the Lord's Day, Francisco was wandering about the valley, poking into fox holes and rabbit burrows. He caught a lizard and set it on the back of his hand, taking great care, however, not to hurt or frighten it. When the girls had said the last Glory be to the Father and put their rosaries back in their pockets, Francisco sauntered back to them.

"Look what I've found!" he cried gleefully, showing them a little green snake which was coiled around his shepherd's staff.

"Oh, perhaps it's poisonous and will bite us!" cried his sister.

"Ah, no, it won't bite," he said, "but I'm sure it's

thirsty." Off he ran, got some milk from one of the ewes, brought it back on a hollow stone and gave it to the snake to drink.

After freeing the snake, Francisco peered around with his hand over his eyes, looking for something else of interest. Suddenly he called out to the two girls: "The sheep keep going into the broom bushes over there, and you know we need those bushes for making brooms. We can't keep them out, so wouldn't it be a good plan to build a little wall around the bushes?"

"Oh, yes, let's build a little wall!" cried Jacinta eagerly. So the little girls collected the stones, and Francisco carefully built them up in a circle around the broom bushes.

The hard work made them hungry, so Francisco opened the bag he had been carrying on his shoulder, and, after saying a short grace, the children started to eat heartily. They threw a few bits of bread to the sheep, too, and of course Jacinta fed Snowflake with special care. After their meal they continued to work on the wall. They loved building more than anything else and already had built little houses and grottoes to shelter themselves from the sun. But it became warmer and warmer and soon the three builders sat down for a rest under a shady evergreen oak.

"I'm tired," declared Francisco, lying down flat on his back and pulling his cap over his eyes. "You two keep an eye on the sheep!"

"You old sleepyhead!" cried his sister, who would have liked him to play a merry tune.

Suddenly the girls were startled from their rest. Far away on the horizon a flash of lightning had lighted up the blue sky!

"There's a thunderstorm coming, Francisco!" cried Lucia, shaking her cousin awake.

"Don't be silly! There's not a single cloud in the sky," grumbled the boy sitting up and yawning.

"But there was a flash of lightning," Jacinta told him. "There will be thunder at any moment!" But no thunder came, and Francisco was just beginning to pull his cap down over his eyes again and continue his interrupted sleep.

"We had better drive the sheep home," Lucia advised. "In May a storm often blows down from the mountains and ends up in a thunderstorm."

"The leaves of the trees aren't rustling at all," protested the boy, "but if you think we should go home, let's go. I don't mind."

So the children hurriedly gathered their little flock together, and Jacinta took her pet lamb on her shoulder again. They drove the sheep down the hillside and Francisco played his flute as they went.

They were hardly across the valley when they saw a streak of lightning flashing over a low spreading tree only a few paces away from them. The little shepherds stood still, terrified. Then their eyes became riveted on a stunted evergreen oak tree which suddenly had become enveloped in radiant light. A white cloud was resting right over its crown. Now the girls could see a Lady of supernatural beauty hovering in the golden light over the branches of the tree. Her face was indescribably beautiful, and her snow-white gown reached to her feet. Her hands were folded on her breast, and in her right hand she held rosary beads of exquisite pearls.

"Do not be afraid. I will not do you any harm," they heard a silvery, bell-like voice saying.

"Who are you?" stammered Lucia at last.

"I come from heaven," was the answer.

"You come from heaven?" exclaimed the ten-year-old

girl. "Oh, then do please tell me if I shall go to heaven, too!"

"Yes, you shall certainly go to heaven!"

"And Jacinta, too?"

"Yes, Jacinta, too."

"And Francisco?"

"Yes, also Francisco," replied the Lady, smiling. "But he too must say many rosaries."

The boy, who did not hear the voice and saw nothing but the radiant light, tugged Lucia's sleeve and asked, surprised, "Who are you talking to? What are you saying into the air? Is it the angel?"

"Francisco doesn't see you at all, Senhora," Lucia explained to the apparition.

"He must pray. Then he will see me."

"Get your rosary, quick!" Jacinta whispered to her brother. The boy pulled the beads out of his pocket and began to pray confusedly. He had hardly finished the first Hail Mary when his voice faltered, for now he too could see the beautiful Lady hovering above the branches.

"Oh, how lovely!" he stammered.

"Ask the Lady if she's hungry," Jacinta whispered to her cousin. "We still have some corn bread and a piece of cheese."

But Lucia, probably thinking that it was not proper to offer the beautiful Lady bread and cheese, asked hesitantly, "Senhora, could you please tell me if Maria Rosario, José das Neves' daughter, is in heaven, too?"

"Yes, she is."

"And her sister Amelia?"

The Lady suddenly looked a little sad. "She is still in purgatory," she replied. "You must pray for her."

Lucia's eyes filled with tears, but now the heavenly Lady began to speak again.

"Would you like to offer yourselves to God, to make sacrifices, and to accept willingly all the sufferings which He may send you, in order to make reparation for the many sins which offend God, to obtain the conversion of sinners, and to make amends for all the outrages which are committed against the Immaculate Heart of Mary?"

"Yes, indeed, gladly, Senhora!" Lucia assured her.

"Oh, indeed I will!" Jacinta promised too.

"You will have to suffer a great deal," the wonderful voice continued, "but God will always help you by His grace, and give you comfort."

At these words the Lady spread out her hands and a golden shimmer seemed to fall from them down on the children. The three little shepherds fell on their knees and prayed as fervently as they could.

"Say the rosary every day with devotion and come here at this same hour on the thirteenth of each month! Then I will tell you who I am and what I want of you!"

Lucia, remembering the sermon she had heard in Boleiros, gathered up all her courage and asked, "Could you please tell me, Senhora, if the war will be over soon?"

"I shall not tell you that yet," replied the beautiful Lady. Then she raised her hands once more as if in blessing and disappeared into the silver clouds toward the east.

The children gazed after the strange light as long as there was a trace of it to be seen. Then everything was as before. The sun shone brightly in the sky, and the Cova da Iria looked just as it always did in the quiet noonday hours.

"The sheep!" cried Francisco, who was the first to come back to earth. "Oh, heavens! They've gone into the pea fields." And he ran into the neighboring fields and drove the animals out with his stick.

"They haven't done any harm at all!" said Jacinta, who together with her cousin had followed Francisco.

"I knew they wouldn't have," said Lucia, who was still in an enraptured state. "The heavenly Lady would not have allowed them to."

"How is it," asked the puzzled boy, "that I saw the beautiful Lady but didn't hear what she said?"

"Didn't you hear her?" asked Jacinta, surprised. "Why, she spoke just like Father and Mother speak!"

"It's strange," murmured Francisco thoughtfully.

"Oh, how beautiful she was!" cried Jacinta again and again as they drove the flock back to the pasture.

They sat down on the stone wall that they had built, and Francisco made his sister and his cousin tell him word for word everything that the heavenly Lady had said to them. When he was told that he too would go to heaven if he said the rosary zealously, he jumped up and clapping his hands cried, "Oh, dear Lady from heaven, I'll say the rosary from now on as often as you like!"

"But who can she have been?" asked Jacinta, thoughtfully caressing her lamb.

"Don't you know?" asked Lucia. "Why, it was Our Lady herself! I'm quite sure of that, even though she didn't tell us her name."

"I believe that, too. She was just a little bit like the picture of Our Lady of Mount Carmel in the church in Fatima," said the boy.

"Yes, you're right! She was," said Lucia. "Look here, Jacinta," she added after a few moments, "please don't say a word to another soul about this. No one would believe us, and people would only say we had invented it all. And you, too, Francisco, don't breathe a word, not even to your father and mother!"

"I promise I won't say a word," said the boy. "You can't talk about a thing like that, anyway. But I wonder if Jacinta will keep her mouth shut. She's a chatterbox and can't hold her tongue."

"I promise I won't say a word to anyone!" the little one assured them indignantly. "I didn't say a word to anyone the time we saw the angel, and now I certainly won't tell."

"Who knows? Perhaps you won't," said Francisco, shrugging his shoulders.

When the shadows of the trees grew longer, the children returned home with their flock. They walked in silence, wrapped in their own thoughts.

Again they met the village piper.

"Well, Francisco, what's come over you that you're not playing the flute?" asked Luis, laughing.

"I can't always be playing," replied the boy evasively.

"Remember the flute I've promised you," the merry fellow reminded him.

"Yes, I'll come and fetch it," replied Francisco, but he did not sound as enthusiastic as he had in the morning.

"I can't imagine what's happened to you, you're all so changed! Well, get along home quickly; I'm sure you're hungry. *Ate logo*, Francisco! Good-by for now!"

The children separated the sheep in front of the Marto's house. The brother and sister drove theirs into the pen and Lucia went on home with hers.

During supper the Marto children were very silent and picked at their potatoes and salad without much appetite.

"What on earth is the matter with you?" asked their mother, looking at her youngest children with surprise.

"Ah, nothing at all," replied Francisco evasively.

"Eat your supper. You must surely be hungry."

"Let them alone, Mother. They're just a bit tired," said their father Manuel, laughing. "It was hot today."

After supper the whole family went to the May devotions in the church. When they returned, the father suggested that the family sit in the garden for a while.

"Perhaps Mother has a little glass of wine for me," he hinted. "José may have a glass, too. And a little drop won't do you any harm either," he said to his wife.

While the father and children sat on the garden bench, the mother went into the kitchen to fetch the earthenware jug of wine. Jacinta slipped in behind her.

"Well, what is it, child?" asked the mother when she saw her.

The child remained silent for a moment. Then, unable to restrain herself any longer, she flung her arms around her mother's neck and cried: "Oh, Mother, we saw the Blessed Virgin in the Cova da Iria today! She was most wonderfully beautiful and she spoke to us!"

Her mother almost let the jug fall, she received such a shock. "What on earth are you talking about, Jacinta?" she asked sharply. "Have you gone crazy?"

"But it's true, Mother; you know I don't tell lies," said the little girl, flushing. "I really saw her, and Francisco and Lucia saw her, too!"

"Call Francisco!"

The boy looked at his sister distrustfully when she called him. "Have you told?" he whispered.

"Ah, Francisco, I had to let it out. I couldn't keep it to myself any longer," stammered Jacinta.

"Now you've got us into a nice pickle!" said the boy.

But it was all out in any case, so he corroborated to his mother all that his little sister had told her.

"But good heavens! Only the saints have ever seen the Mother of God on earth," cried Senhora Olimpia, bewildered, "and of course Bernadette of Lourdes, too. Yes, she saw her, but she was a thousand times more pious than you are. The Blessed Virgin doesn't appear to naughty little children such as you."

"We didn't want to tell anyone, not even you, Mother," declared the boy. "But when you ask me, I have to tell the truth. Or would you want me to tell a lie?"

"No, no!" cried the woman, clasping her head between her hands. "I have never allowed you to tell lies. But you have surely been dreaming, children; it was such a hot day!"

"How could all three of us have had the same dream? You don't really think that yourself, Mother. No, no! What we have told you is true. Lucia can tell you, too."

"Aren't you bringing the wine, wife?" Manuel called in from the garden.

"Yes, I'm coming!" replied Olimpia. Then she warned the children not to tell anyone else for the time. No one would believe such silly stories, she said.

But when she and her husband were going to bed that night, she told him the strange tale. He listened, puzzled. Then he said, "I really don't know what to make of it. The children are truthful. Perhaps someone has been playing some daft joke on them!"

"That would have been a bad joke indeed!" muttered Olimpia.

"Well, let us sleep on it! The children will be sure to have something else in their heads tomorrow. And you could have a talk with Lucia, but it's best to keep Maria-Rosa out of it. I'm afraid she would take a stick to the child straightaway, for she couldn't stand any joking in religious matters."

"Neither could I even if I wouldn't take a broomstick to them," replied the woman resolutely.

"Well, let's sleep on it," said the husband again, yawning. "I'm tired and I have to be up early."

Francisco said another rosary in bed long after João, with whom he shared a room, was snoring. Then he too fell asleep.

Jacinta did not sleep for a long time. The happiness of the day kept her awake. Her bed was beside the little window and she gazed up at the sky where the stars and the silver crescent moon were shining.

"Our Lady's lamp!" she whispered into the darkness when she saw the moon. "How lovely it is, but the Blessed Virgin, who appeared to us, is a thousand times lovelier!"

It was a long time before she fell asleep, but even in her dreams she kept crying: "Oh, how beautiful she is! The heavenly Lady!"

Teresa, who slept with her, woke up, then she wakened her sister and asked, "Who are you talking about, little one?"

"Who am I talking about?" asked Jacinta drowsily.

"Yes, who's the beautiful Lady you were talking about in your dream?"

"Ah, if I only knew!" murmured Jacinta dreamily. Then she fell asleep again.

She must have been dreaming! thought Teresa. Then she too turned over and dropped off once more.

❧ 3 ❧

RUMORS IN THE VILLAGE

The following morning Senhora Olimpia turned up at the Santos' house before the children had set off for the pastures, and asked for Lucia.

"What's the matter?" asked Maria-Rosa, who was cooking a pot of pigs' food on the low hearth. The kitchen was so full of smoke that the woman's eyes were full of tears. "Has she been up to any mischief?" she asked.

"Oh, no. Not at all. I only want to ask her something," replied Senhora Marto evasively.

"Lucia!" called the mother to her daughter who was out in the yard feeding the fowls. "What have you to ask my child so urgently?" she asked Olimpia.

"Didn't she tell you anything?"

"About what?" asked Maria-Rosa, who was blowing the fire, for the damp wood was not lighting well.

"I mean about what happened in the Cova da Iria."

"What happened there?" asked her sister-in-law straightening up. "Lucia, what happened yesterday in the Cova da Iria?"

The girl, who was just coming into the kitchen, stopped

on the threshold, turned pale, and pressed her hands to her breast.

"Couldn't you come into the yard, Auntie?" she stammered hesitantly. "There's so much smoke here."

"Very well, but I'm coming, too," said her mother determinedly. "After all, it concerns me too if you've been up to any mischief."

"We haven't done anything wrong, Mother," the child assured her.

"Now tell me what's the matter!" cried the mother, looking from her daughter to her sister-in-law.

"The children say they have seen the Blessed Virgin," explained Olimpia hesitantly, though her niece was silently entreating her not to tell.

"What nonsense is this?" cried Lucia's mother angrily. "You seem to allow your children to tell you fairy tales, Olimpia. If one of mine came and told me such inventions, I would soon teach her not to lie to her mother! Hurry up, Lucia. Tell your aunt at once that it's not true!"

"But it *is* true!" declared Lucia, now as white as a sheet.

Her mother, who had turned back toward the kitchen, wheeled around abruptly and stared at her daughter. "Surely you don't say that the Blessed Virgin appeared to you in the Cova da Iria?" she asked in a low menacing voice. "Admit at once that you have told a lie!"

"I cannot, Mother. It's the truth," replied Lucia tremulously.

"Indeed? Well then tell us about it!" ordered the mother.

Lucia took a deep breath, then began to tell what had happened. As she spoke she forgot her fears, and her voice became steadier and steadier. Her plain face became almost beautiful and a wonderful light lit up her eyes as she repeated the words of the Mother of God. When she had finished she passed her hand over her forehead as if trying to remember where she was and to whom she had been telling everything.

Senhora Santos stared at the child, bewildered. Once or twice she tried to speak, but she could not utter a word.

"It's strange," said Senhora Olimpia. "Francisco and Jacinta have told me word for word the selfsame story."

Meanwhile her sister-in-law had pulled herself together and now she burst out angrily: "So you actually believe this silly story, Olimpia? I don't want to hear another word about it. If I do, Lucia, you will pay for it! Have children ever before dared to tell their parents such terrible lies?"

"What's all this noise about, so early in the morning?" cried Farmer Antonio Santos, who had just appeared at the kitchen door.

"This silly Lucia says she saw the Blessed Virgin at the Cova da Iria," replied his wife, who was still beside herself with indignation.

"Oh, indeed!" replied the peasant with a chuckle. "That's fine news first thing in the morning. You must have little to do, child, to be talking such nonsense. Get the breakfast, wife; I'm hungry." And he turned back to the house, muttering to himself: "Women's chatter, of course!"

Poor Jacinta met with bitter reproaches when the three little shepherds set off for the Gouveia pasture that morning.

"See what you have done!" lamented Lucia. "Mother is very angry."

"Didn't I say that Jacinta is a chatterbox and can't keep her mouth shut?" muttered Francisco, kicking a pebble.

"I didn't want to say a word," protested the child, in tears. "I wasn't going to say anything at all, but something inside me made me want to tell Mother."

"Well, perhaps it isn't so bad," said her brother kindly. "We won't tell anyone and our parents will keep quiet about it, too. Nothing bad can happen then."

That evening at supper the Santos family were all rather depressed. Lucia did not open her lips, and the mother had no appetite and soon pushed away her plate. After the meal the boys and girls got busy on their various jobs in the stables and yard.

"I'm going out to take a breath of air," said the father putting on his cap.

"Don't drink too much," his wife warned him. "If you do you will say foolish things again."

"If only the womenfolk didn't say so many foolish things," retorted the farmer with a grin and a glance at Lucia. And saying this he went off.

Antonio Guimarães' Dão wine tasted good after the hot day. Farmer Santos became merrier and more talkative with every glass. The men talked about the weather, and the prospects for the harvest, sickness among the livestock and the people, the parish priest, the war, and a thousand other things. The cobbler Farzeria grumbled about his gout and his wife's ill humor, and tossed off one brandy after another to console himself.

"Yes, indeed! The women are a caution!" chuckled Antonio. "The fancies they get into their heads sometimes! You'd hardly believe it, but my old woman told me quite seriously that the Virgin Mary appeared to my Lucia in the Cova da Iria."

"What did she say?" asked the tavern keeper, astounded.

"Didn't I tell you? My old woman said the Blessed Virgin appeared to my youngest little girl—that she saw her hovering over an evergreen oak like a balloon. Extraordinary ideas women get into their heads!"

"The Blessed Virgin is no air balloon, neighbor!" cried the shoemaker indignantly. He was already more than a little drunk. "I'm not very pious, and I don't keep on the heels of the priest like some of the women do, but I won't listen to anything like that, even from you, Antonio!"

"You fool, you've got me all wrong!" replied Antonio angrily. "I never said the Mother of God was an air balloon!"

The two men were just coming to blows when they were distracted by a burst of loud hearty laughter from the doorway, and Luis, the wandering musician, walked in.

"Things look pretty lively here. What's come between you two that you're going for each other like a pair of fighting cocks?" he asked. Soon he too heard the whole story.

"That's certainly news," he said, stroking his chin. "You say the Virgin Mary appeared in the Cova da Iria, and to your daughter moreover, Antonio? Well I must say that's rare news."

"I tell you it's women's chatter!" cried Antonio vehemently. "But if she did appear, why shouldn't it be to my child? Isn't my Lucia just as good as anyone else? I tell you she is, and much better!" He talked and talked, and got so worked up that in the end he didn't know what he was saying. "Anyway she doesn't tell lies as you do, Luis. Everyone in the village knows that you tell lies, and that you steal fowl, too!"

"I don't deny that I do wring the neck of a chicken now and then when it comes my way," said the joker, laughing. "And so help me I couldn't say that I have never told a lie in my life!"

"But my Lucia doesn't tell lies, do you hear!" repeated Antonio staggering toward the piper.

"What about when she said that the Mother of God was an air balloon?" babbled the shoemaker, half to himself.

"Who said that?" cried the farmer. "If she said she saw her, then she did see her, just as surely as Bernadette of Lourdes saw her! I didn't know Bernadette, of course, but I'm certain she was no better than my Lucia."

"Don't quarrel, neighbors. Better drink another glass," said Guimarães, trying to make peace. But the shoemaker kept on about the air balloon, and finally wept loudly over the alleged defamation of the Mother of God.

"That's certainly strange news, Antonio," the piper repeated. "But you're quite right. Why shouldn't the Mother of God appear to your daughter as well as to anyone else's child? Indeed you're quite right. Lucia is a good little girl who well deserves to see the Blessed Virgin. And now let's have a drink on it, neighbor!"

As Antonio walked home late that night he realized that he had been talking foolishly in the pub.

His wife eyed him suspiciously when he came into their room. "You haven't let out anything about the Cova da Iria in the tavern, have you?" she asked him.

"Not a word!" the farmer assured her. "Anyway, I haven't been to the Cova da Iria."

"No, but you've been to old Guimarães' tavern. Heaven knows what you've been talking about there again."

"I haven't talked about anything at all. I didn't open my lips the whole evening," protested Antonio once more.

Maria-Rosa put out the light and lay down to sleep full of forebodings.

A few days later the whole village was gossiping about the apparition. Carolina, the youngest but one of the Santos children, came home from school crying and told her mother that she had been laughed at in the street on account of Lucia. "I can't bear to go outside the house any more!" she said in a flood of tears.

"There must be an end of this!" said the mother firmly. "I'll go to the parish priest on Sunday."

But the three little shepherds had an even worse time than their brothers and sisters. As they drove their flocks out to the fields, they were shouted at from every side:

"Look! There go the storytellers!"

"What fine new tales are you thinking up?"

"Oh, look! There's Our Blessed Lady walking over the roofs!"

Lucia made no reply. Jacinta, a little frightened, pressed her Snowflake to her breast. Francisco would have loved to give the boys a few good whacks with his shepherd's staff, but then he reflected that all this was probably part of the suffering that the Blessed Virgin had foretold for them. So he pretended not to hear anything and went his way quietly. Sometimes, too, he played his sugar-cane flute.

The wandering musician who, as everyone knew, hardly ever set foot in a church, was the only person who, in his half-bantering, half-indulgent way, tried to comfort the children.

"Let the young pups talk as much as they like; don't take any notice of them. And if it would help you at all, I'll tell everyone that I believe in your apparition."

"But do you really believe in it?" asked Jacinta incredulously.

"Ah, that's the trouble!" said the piper, scratching his head. "I'd like so much to help you, but . . ."

"Well, you don't believe in the apparition, so it's no use saying you do," replied Francisco, crestfallen.

The Martos family too were very much annoyed about the gossip that was going on in the village.

"I really don't know what to think," said Olimpia, sighing. "After all, the children have never yet lied to me!"

"Yes, that's just it," replied her husband Manuel Pedro. "And have you noticed that the little ones are much more obedient now, and say their prayers far more fervently than they used to? There must be something in it."

"You surely don't believe in it?" cried his wife.

"I don't know what I believe," admitted Manuel Pedro, shaking his head and going out to the yard.

Senhora Santos, meanwhile, was as determined as ever to put an end to the wretched story. Every evening she took Lucia aside and explained to her what a grave sin it was to make fun of anything holy. And when her words seemed to have no effect, she took a cane and beat her little girl unmercifully.

"Now will you tell the truth?" she would gasp, exhausted from the exertion of inflicting the punishment.

"But I *am* telling the truth!" the poor child would wail. "The Blessed Virgin really did appear to us."

"If you continue to lie like that I'll put you into a dark hole and leave you there until you come to your senses."

The following Sunday she went to the parish priest after High Mass and told him her trouble.

"Of course I have heard the story, too," said the priest,

"and I simply don't understand it. After all, Lucia is a good pious child, and the same can be said of the Marto children. How on earth did they get such an idea?"

"That's what I keep asking myself all the time," said the woman, sighing. "Again and again I have warned Lucia to tell the truth, and I have punished her severely many times. But she still insists that the Blessed Virgin appeared to her and the Marto children."

"My dear woman, this matter cannot be cleared up with the help of a stick. The children undoubtedly believe what they say. I'm only wondering how they got this idea. Well, I think I must have a talk with Lucia myself sometime."

"Yes, please do, Your Reverence!" replied the farmer's wife eagerly.

"Meanwhile leave Lucia in peace and put away your rod," the priest advised her as he accompanied her to the door.

"To think that such a misfortune should befall me!" lamented the woman as she went down the steps.

The days passed and the hot month of June arrived. It was the twelfth of the month, the eve of the feast of St. Anthony of Padua, who with Our Lady of the Seven Joys was patron saint of Fatima. His feast was always celebrated by the whole parish. After High Mass there was a solemn procession and all the peasants from far and near attended in their best attire, riding beribboned donkeys or driving in decorated carts. Those who were comfortably off gave bread and sausages to the poor so that no one should go hungry on that day. In the afternoon the musicians played up in the little stone gallery in the front of the church, and young and old danced the fandango, shouting merrily as they whirled round. Old Guimarães saw to it that no one went thirsty in the heat. He set up a small outdoor booth of his own and served the best Dão wine. It was no wonder that everyone looked forward to the feast for many days.

"Get out your festival dress—the white skirt and the embroidered bodice," Maria-Rosa reminded her youngest daughter the evening before. "Tomorrow we are going to the St. Anthony Festival."

"But tomorrow will be the thirteenth," Lucia reminded her, blushing, "and I must go to the Cova da Iria. Ah, do please come with me, Mother. You're sure to see the Blessed Virgin, too!"

"Are you starting that nonsensical story again?" her mother burst out angrily. "Of course I'm going to the parish festival, and you're coming with me."

"But St. Anthony isn't beautiful at all," protested Lucia, thinking of the crude statue in the parish church at Fatima. No, the rough, thickset saint with his bald head was not at all beautiful!

"The Blessed Virgin is a thousand times more beautiful," she said.

"You're coming with me to the festival," declared her mother firmly. "Manuel and Gloria will drive the sheep to the pastures in the morning. They will come home early and then they can come to the church square with us."

Lucia did not dare to oppose her mother's wishes further.

The Marto family too were making their plans for the following day.

"Mother and I are going to the market in Pedeiras to buy two oxen," said the father. "Florinda and Teresa will drive the sheep out to the pastures. You others may go to the festival."

"May we go to the beautiful Lady in the Cova da Iria," begged Jacinta, nestling coaxingly against her father.

"Do as you wish," replied Manuel, who could not refuse the little girl her heart's desire.

"You should have forbidden them to go there," said Olimpia to her husband afterward.

"Ah, there's no harm done. The children will certainly see nothing tomorrow, and that will be the end of the whole story."

"Perhaps you're right," said his wife.

Maria-Rosa probably thought the same, for when Lucia again begged her next morning to allow her to go to the Cova da Iria, she did not refuse her.

Accordingly, after early Mass, the three little shepherds set out in silence to keep their appointment with their heavenly visitant. They were terribly surprised when they found that about fifty people were following them. Some of these people were only coming out of curiosity, and they now started to mock the children. But there were others who came in all sincerity because they felt a spark of hope that heaven might look down in mercy on their sorrows and needs. And last of all, behind all the others, came poor Luisa Bernardos. Perhaps she was the only one besides the children who truly believed.

Just before they arrived in the valley, a grief-stricken old woman came up to Lucia and whispered to her: "If it is true that Our Blessed Lady appears to you, do please ask her to cure my son. He has tuberculosis and he is spitting blood. The doctor has given him up, but perhaps . . ."

"Yes, I will ask help for him," replied Lucia, deeply touched.

❧ 4 ❧

THE FEAST OF ST. ANTHONY

The children sat down in the shade of the big oak tree through which the lightning had flashed a month before, while the other people who had come lay around on the grass waiting for the miracle. It was warm, and not a puff of wind stirred the branches. A few little girls from Aljustrel and Boleiros joined the children, and they all began innocently playing together. Toward midday they started to recite the rosary. They had just finished the fifth Glorious Mystery, the Coronation of Our Lady in Heaven, when a streak of lightning flashed across the cloudless sky.

"She's coming!" cried Lucia, jumping up. And the three children ran over to the evergreen oak over which they had seen the heavenly apparition before.

"There she is!" cried Jacinta, radiant with joy.

"Where? Where is she?" her companions asked.

"Don't you see her? She's hovering over the tree!"

"How, how lovely she is! How heavenly!"

The bystanders pressed around the three children inquisitively. They saw the green branches bending down as though they were carrying some light but invisible load. But only Francisco, Jacinta and Lucia saw the wonderful Lady who was hovering above the evergreen oak in a flood of light.

Lucia clasped her hands in prayer. "Kind lady, you asked me to come here," she cried in a voice that could be heard at quite a distance. "Please tell me what you want of me."

Only she and Jacinta heard the answer that came down. "Come here on the thirteenth of each month. I also wish you to learn to read."

"A woman asked me to beg you to make her son well," said Lucia. "Oh, do please grant her wish!"

The Blessed Virgin nodded but looked sad as she replied, "He does not yet love God with his whole heart, but if he is converted he will get well before the end of the year."

Remembering all her bitter sufferings, the little girl begged with a sigh: "Oh, dear Senhora, please take us to heaven with you!"

"I shall take Jacinta and Francisco soon," replied the Lady, "but you must remain in the world. Through you Our Saviour will teach men to know me and to love me."

"Am I to be left behind alone, then?" stammered Lucia, dismayed.

"My heart shall be your refuge and the way which shall lead you to God," replied the Lady. Then once more she spread out her hands, and Lucia noticed that the celestial light enveloped Jacinta and Francisco. She alone remained untouched by its radiance.

The bystanders saw the silvery cloud that had been hovering over the evergreen oak suddenly move eastward. At the same time all the branches bent in the same direction as though the hem of a cloak had touched them lightly in passing. All the people as well as the three children remained gazing fixedly at the cloud until it disappeared into the clear sky.

"My God, I believe! I believe!" cried Maria Carreira, a woman from the nearby village of Moita.

"I believe! I believe!" cried many others, too.

But some shook their heads and said, "What is all this about? The wind has merely blown through the branches. That's all!"

"But there's not a breath of wind!" the believing pointed out. "Just look! Not a leaf is moving on the trees!"

The woman who had asked Lucia to put in a word for her son was breathless with agitation as she asked what the Mother of God had said. When she was told, she replied almost inaudibly: "That's quite true. My son has not always been good, but now he will love God and the Blessed Virgin. And then he will get well again."

Lucia's two elder sisters, Maria and Teresa, whom the mother had sent to watch the children, had been looking on from a distance at all that was happening. They had not dared to come any nearer because they feared the jibes of the unbelieving. Now they went home in silence. When their mother asked them what had happened, they were unable to answer for a long time. At last the elder said:

"It was all so strange and solemn, just like in church. It was as though God had passed by near us. Perhaps there really was an apparition, and perhaps it is a great miracle."

"So you are beginning to lose your senses, too!" said the mother shaking her head.

The three children had great difficulty in getting away from the crowd. They wanted to be alone with each other to talk about what had happened. At last Lucia was able to tell Francisco what the Blessed Virgin had said. For this time too the boy had heard nothing, to his great disappointment.

"Am I going to die?" he asked, turning pale, and for a few moments he gazed pensively across the vast countryside that was bathed in the summer sunshine.

"But Our Lady said we would go to heaven," Jacinta reminded him.

"Yes, to heaven," repeated the boy, and now a glow of joy passed over his sunburned face. "Then we shall be able to see her all the time, and Our Lord, too. No! I'm not sad any more!"

Lucia explained that she did not think Our Lady wished them to tell this revelation to anyone. They should keep it a secret always.

"I'm afraid Mother would be terribly sad if she knew we are to die soon," said Jacinta thoughtfully. "Well, I certainly won't tell anything this time."

Francisco looked at her distrustfully. "Are you quite sure?" he asked.

"Yes, I'm quite sure! You'll see!"

And this time she kept her promise! It wasn't until ten years later that Lucia divulged the secret, when she was miraculously inspired by God with permission to do so.

At last the children walked slowly home, reciting the rosary. Only poor Luisa Bernardos remained in the Cova when all the rest of the people had left. She threw herself on her knees in front of the tree over which the apparition had appeared, and prayed to her heavenly Mother in her misery.

Farmer Marto and his wife returned home from the market late in the afternoon. The children told them at once of the second miraculous apparition, but they did not tell their own special secret. Their mother listened to the story much puzzled, and then went about her work in silence. Manuel Pedro got the children to tell him everything all over again. Only when they had done so did he put the oxen he had bought away in the stable.

After finishing his chores, he sat on the garden bench for a long time thinking, with his head in his hands. "I almost believe the children are telling the truth," he said to his wife when he came into the house at last.

"But could such a miracle happen to *them?*" asked Olimpia, bewildered. Her husband did not reply.

Meanwhile the festival was in full swing on the church square of Fatima. The people danced and amused themselves until sunset. Then, when hundreds of little Chinese lanterns lighted up the square, the festival spirit rose still higher. Antonio Guimarães looked thoroughly pleased, because dancing made people thirsty, and the merrymakers were drinking plenty of his Dão wine. The musicians who had come from Vila Nova de Ourém kept the celebration going fast and furiously with their lively music. The older folk, who had shared in the fun as long as they were able, gradually dropped out and retired to the innkeeper's booth to spend the rest of the night over their wine. Someone mentioned the new apparition in the Cova da Iria, and a spirited discussion of the strange event followed.

"I tell you it's all lies and humbug!" cried José Farzeria, the shoemaker. "The time when saints appeared to people is long past. Heaven no longer troubles about the earth. Otherwise the war would have ended long ago, and I would have been cured of my gout."

"What about going to the Cova da Iria sometime?" said the village piper, who had been playing with the other musicians and was having a little rest. "Who knows? Perhaps the Blessed Virgin might cure your crooked joints."

"I tell you it's all lies and humbug!" shouted another. "If I were Antonio Santos I'd knock the nonsense out of my daughter even if I had to beat her black and blue!"

"Here he comes! You can tell him that to his face!" someone said, pointing to Farmer Santos, who was walking unsteadily toward the booth.

"What should he tell me?" asked Antonio. "Are you talking about my Lucia again? She's none of your business, do you hear! She's nothing to anyone. She's my business and mine alone!"

"I would be ashamed to be staggering about drunk if my daughter were fooling the whole neighborhood!" cried Gomez, the village barber.

"You should give her a few cuppings!" said someone to the barber. "Perhaps she has too much blood from her father."

"What's that you're saying?" roared Antonio. "Put a few leeches on your own snout! Then perhaps you won't talk such nonsense!"

"Don't quarrel, folks!" said the musician. "Just look over there. The fireworks are starting."

The musicians played a flourish on their trumpets, and a couple of dozen rockets rose up into the night sky with a crackling and whistling sound. The roar of the mortars and the explosions of the fireworks made such a terrific din that the quarreling men could no longer hear their own voices. Antonio Guimarães breathed a sigh of relief, for without this distraction the hotheaded fellows would probably have come to blows and his jugs and glasses would have been smashed.

Dom Marcus, the parish priest of Fatima, stood on the

open balcony of his rectory, watching the noisy crowd with much displeasure. How can people dance and yell like that in such sad times? he thought. Will humanity ever come to its senses? He grimly decided to give his parishioners a piece of his mind from the pulpit on Sunday. His words would strike like thunder and lightning, for this behavior was surely provoking God's anger. He looked sadly over toward the faint red light that showed through the chancel window. "Lord, forgive them, for they know not what they do," he prayed.

Then he recalled with pain and misgiving the strange events in the Cova da Iria. He too had heard of the second apparition, but in his life as a priest he had experienced far too many disillusionments to be able to believe that this was a miracle of grace. Who knew what might be behind it all? He could not accept the theory that the children were deliberately lying. But perhaps someone else had a finger in the pie, namely, the devil, who sows the seeds of confusion everywhere in order to reap the harvest afterward. He gets hold of the rowdy, drunken crowd down there in the church square by means of wine and dance music, and he deceives the pious with pseudocelestial visitations. Yes, that must be the explanation. The devil was carrying on his blasphemous activities in the Cova da Iria!

"I wish I were not parish priest of Fatima," sighed Dom Marcus. And as the last rocket exploded beneath the pale stars of the summer night, he made the sign of the cross and went indoors.

❧ 5 ❧

COULD IT BE THE DEVIL?

The next day arrived dull and gloomy and veiled in clouds as though to do penance for the fact that the people, through sheer enthusiasm, had celebrated the feast of St. Anthony in such a wild and disorderly fashion.

While the village was still sleeping, Luisa Bernardos made her way through the silent lanes to the well, with a brown earthenware pitcher on her head. Actually, the well was only a cistern in which the rain water was collected, for there were no living springs in the limestone of Fatima. She had hoped that she would not meet anyone at this early hour, but there were several girls at the well already, apparently having a good morning gossip. They suddenly fell silent as Luisa approached, and replied to her greeting with a chilly *"Bom Dia!"* For these pious folk found it most provoking that a person such as she should draw water from the same well as they.

None of them helped her to work the heavy beam by which the pitcher was let down, nor to lift it on to her head when filled, a service none of the girls would ever refuse to another. But this morning Luisa was hardly conscious of the unfriendliness that by now she had become used to. After a brief greeting, she was about to start for home when one of the girls called out to her mockingly, "You were at the Cova da Iria yesterday. Perhaps you saw the Blessed Virgin, too?"

"No, I did not see her," replied the outcast, "but I know that she was there, and all of you should believe that, too."

"Yes, we do believe firmly in the apparition," replied another girl giggling. "Perhaps she'll get you a husband so your child will have a father!"

Luisa walked away without a word while the horrible hypocritical laughter echoed behind her.

Soon the news that the sinner, of all people, believed in the apparition spread around the village, and there was plenty of malicious comment.

"So you see the kind of people who are running to the Cova!" they were saying in every lane. And in the taverns the talk of the men became more and more ribald and blasphemous.

But Luis, the wandering piper, scratched his stubbly chin and said; "I can't remember much of the Bible any more, but I have an idea that there were publicans and sinners among Our Lord's followers."

"Surely you are not comparing Luisa with St. Mary Magdalen?" growled the shoemaker.

"No, of course I'm not," replied the musician, "for Mary Magdalen was a great sinner, but Luisa is better than most of the women in the village."

"It's easy to see you have no religion," retorted the barber indignantly.

"That may be," said the musician calmly, "but if your slander is religion, I'm glad I haven't any!" And saying this he threw a few escudos on the table for the tavern keeper, took up his mouth organ, and left the pub playing a merry tune.

"Don't be vexed, Senhores," said old Guimarães to the indignant customers. "Everyone knows the kind of fool the piper is."

And so, very soon, people felt sure that, apart from a few superstitious folk, only outcasts and fools believed in the apparitions, and the slanderous talk increased.

The three little shepherds had to suffer a great deal from the public mood. When they drove their little flock through the lanes of Aljustrel, the boys followed them laughing and jeering and making nasty jokes. One woman opened her window every time they passed, and shaking her fist, hurled the most horrible curses and abuse after them. During this time the children preferred to drive their sheep to the desolate stony pastures of Valinhos, where they met hardly a soul except a few other shepherds. In the stone cave of Cabeço, where they had once seen the angel, they prayed earnestly for strength to endure the suffering and trouble.

"Don't worry about all that," Lucia said to the two others again and again. "Remember that the Mother of God told us we should bear everything in atonement for sinners."

They found peace and regained their childish spirits in the quietness of the stony hills. But pious people, mostly from the neighboring villages, sought them out even in the desolate regions of Valinhos and wanted to hear the whole story from their own lips. They asked to hear word for word what the Blessed Virgin had said, and some even wrote down what the children told them.

Lucia usually hid behind the crags when she saw anyone

coming, Francisco became very silent, but Jacinta replied to the questions with childish candor. Sometimes she even enjoyed tantalizing the people a little. To one superior lady of Moita, who was not satisfied with what she had been told, but insisted that the Blessed Virgin must have said a lot more, Jacinta replied:

"Yes, she did say more, but that is a secret we won't tell anyone."

"I will give you ten escudos if you tell me," the lady promised.

Pretending to be tempted, Jacinta replied, "You have such a lovely pearl necklace! Will you give it to me if I tell the secret?"

"Oh, yes, my child!" replied the lady eagerly, taking off her string of pearls.

But the little minx only laughed and said, "Keep it, Senhora! I wouldn't tell you any more even if you gave me a thousand necklaces!"

But alas, the little imp had already revealed far too much, for soon everyone was asking, either seriously or mockingly, what the strange secret was that nobody was to be told.

"There, you've done something stupid again, you little chatterbox," grumbled Francisco. "As though things were not bad enough already!"

"I'll never talk to anyone about it again," the child promised, very much ashamed of herself, her eyes filling with tears.

At least at home the Marto children were left in peace. Their parents did not worry them, and they forbade the brothers and sisters to tease the little ones about the story. But it was quite different in the Santos household. The father became more and more surly and ill-humored, and no longer even enjoyed going to the tavern because the everlasting taunts he met with there upset him so much. The pious mother still regarded the whole thing as a wanton game which the children were carrying on, and she was more determined than ever to make Lucia recant her "lies."

One evening at supper she said to her daughter, "We shall go to Mass tomorrow morning, and then we will visit the rectory because the parish priest wishes to speak to you."

"The priest!" stammered Lucia, turning pale.

"You heard me, didn't you?" snapped the mother.

"I wouldn't like to be in your shoes tomorrow morning," said eleven-year-old Carolina, giggling maliciously. "Goodness knows what the priest may do to you!"

"He'll thrash you until your back is black and blue," said Gloria, "and you know what a thick stick he has!"

"The priest gave a terrible hiding to two boys who spat into the holy water font one time," Manuel recalled. "They howled so loud you could hear them right across the square!"

"To tell stories about the Mother of God is much worse than to spit into the holy water font," said Carolina. "Perhaps the priest will beat you until you're dead."

Lucia was unable to swallow a bite of the green beans on her plate. She sat there pale and trembling.

"Leave the child in peace!" said Maria, the eldest. "Don't be frightened, Lucia, and tell the priest everything you know!"

"I shan't mind if the priest gives you a good thrashing," muttered the mother, "if only he makes you give up your lies."

"Stop this idiotic talk right now!" cried the father, banging the table with his fist. "I don't want to hear another word about the silly business."

That same evening Lucia crept out of the house and ran over to the Marto's to tell her trouble. "I don't know what I'm to do," she cried desperately. "Perhaps it's best if we say we have invented it all. Then we shall at least be left in peace again."

"Could you do such a thing?" stammered Jacinta, horrified. "No, Lucia, we dare not do that. You know you would be telling a lie, if you did, and it's a sin to tell a lie."

"I will tell the truth, anyway," said Francisco. "And you know, the priest has told us to come, too. We are going in the morning with Mother."

"Thank God for that," exclaimed their cousin, greatly relieved.

Then the father, Manuel, came in and spoke to the children in his usual quiet, kindly way.

"What are you frightened of?" he asked, smiling. "Why, it won't be as bad as all that. I don't believe the priest will touch you. After all, he's a priest, not an ogre."

The following morning the two mothers set out early with their children.

"You are to kneel down before him and tell him that you have been lying," Senhora Santos ordered her daughter. "He will give you a penance which you will perform. And next Sunday he will announce it from the pulpit, and there will be an end to the apparitions."

"But if I did that I would be telling a lie to the parish priest," cried Lucia vehemently. "No, Mother! I cannot do that. It would be a sin."

"You're to do what your mother tells you!"

That day the Mass came to an end far too quickly for the children. Lucia in particular dreaded what was before her. Her knees were quaking as she climbed up the steps to the door of the rectory.

"Now, you know what you're to say!" her mother whispered to her once more before the door opened. "What a thing to do, indeed! Enticing the people to the Cova da Iria to pray in front of a stunted tree!"

"But they don't have to go there!" protested Lucia desperately.

The parish priest was sitting at the table in his study, with his head resting on his hands when the two mothers came in with their children.

"So here you are!" exclaimed the priest, rousing himself from his reverie. Then looking at the children he said, shaking his head, "Now, what are all these stories you're telling!"

The two mothers kissed the priest's hand respectfully, as the custom was, and the children followed their example. Francisco, who was the calmest of them, looked about the room with curiosity. He had expected that a priest's home would be much grander than this. Why, it was not really much better than their own. The table and the chairs were quite plain, and there was nothing but a wooden crucifix hanging on the whitewashed wall. The books in their bookshelves were the only things in the room which impressed him. No doubt the priest had read them all. With something like horror Francisco thought of the Blessed Virgin's order that he and the girls should learn to read.

The priest sent the Marto children and the two mothers out onto the veranda while he interviewed Lucia. The little girl, who had imagined it would be much more terrifying, related quite candidly what she had seen and heard and replied to Dom Marcus's questions without hesitation. At last the priest sent her out and called in Francisco.

"What do you want to hear, Father?" asked the boy, looking at the priest with shining eyes. "Lies or truth?"

"The truth, of course," replied the priest, looking with approval at the open face of the boy. "Tell me what you know."

Francisco related frankly what he had seen.

"And did you not hear anything?"

"No. The girls told me afterward what Our Lady had said to them."

"That's strange, very strange indeed," murmured Dom Marcus, striding up and down the room.

Finally he called in Jacinta.

The little girl already had done so much mischief with her chatter that she was firmly resolved not to say too much this time. So she answered only yes or no, hardly daring to look at the priest.

Now the priest called the mothers and the other children back to the room.

"I really do not know what to think about it," he said, sitting down heavily. "It does not seem to me to be a manifestation from heaven. I can hardly believe that Our Blessed Lady would come expressly from heaven to tell you that you should say the rosary every day. Every pious family in the parish does that in any case. No, no! It's certainly not a message from God."

He stood up wearily and began to pace up and down again.

"I have not received the impression that the children are telling stories," he said at last, turning to the mothers. "They definitely have seen something, and the two little girls have heard something, too. If all this does not come from God, it can only come from the devil. We read in the Bible that Satan can take the form of an angel in order to mislead the good. Yes, this is certainly the work of the devil, who is seeking to cause unrest and confuse souls."

"I hope you will forbid the children to go to the Cova da Iria any more," suggested Maria-Rosa. But her sister-in-law stood silent, her work-worn hands folded.

"I dare not do that," replied Dom Marcus quietly, "for after all, it might be true, and I could not be responsible for keeping the children away by such an order."

"Yes, but what are we to do, then, Father?" asked Senhora Santos desperately.

"Do what you think best," said the priest with a sigh. "I cannot advise you. Time will show the real facts of the case."

"Now we're just as we were before!" said Maria-Rosa angrily as they left the rectory.

"Let us leave it all in the hands of the good God," replied Senhora Marto placatingly.

"What if it is really the devil who is fooling us?" said Lucia, who was walking ahead with the other children.

"No, we needn't be afraid of that!" declared Jacinta, who had suddenly found her tongue again. "You know that the devil is ugly and hides himself in hell, down under the earth. But the Lady was beautiful, and she came down from heaven and went back there again."

"Yes, you're right," said Lucia, relieved.

"Besides, I never heard of the devil ordering anyone to say the rosary," said Francisco confidently.

But Lucia was unable to rid herself of her frightful doubts. During the long winter evenings she had heard a lot about witchcraft, and about the devil, who often came

—so people said—to fool and delude folk. The priest was a learned man who had studied and who possessed many books. If he thought the devil might be behind it all, well then she would rather have nothing more to do with it.

One night shortly before the 13th of July, she had a most horrible dream. She suddenly saw the flames of hell around her. The devil emerged from the eternal flames and called to her in a horrible voice: "So you have allowed yourself to be deceived by me! You have knelt down before me and prayed to me, and led many others into doing the same. Now you are in my power forever!" And saying this he tried to seize her in his claws. But Lucia shouted so loudly in her sleep that she wakened her sister, who asked her what was the matter.

"Oh, I've had such a terrible dream!" stammered Lucia, still terrified.

"That comes from all your lying stories," replied her sister, turning away from her.

On the 12th of July, Lucia, utterly distraught, slipped off to the Marto's house and said to Francisco and Jacinta, "I'm not going to the Cova tomorrow!"

"But the beautiful Lady told us to come," protested Jacinta horrified.

"Well, I'm not going all the same. If the beautiful Lady asks about me, tell her I was afraid she might be the devil."

"Are you beginning that silly talk again?" said Francisco. "Well, we're going, and if you don't want to come with us, we'll go without you."

"Very well, then. I will speak to the Lady," said Jacinta, bursting into tears.

Lucia crept away, hiding her face with her apron.

That day, people who had heard of the apparition and

wanted to see Lucia, came to Fatima from far and near. But the little girl hid behind a hedge in a neighbor's garden and did not come home until the evening when the people had gone away.

Her mother scolded her violently. "So that's the kind of daughter you are! Instead of minding the sheep you skulk about and hide yourself! My word, you're truly a saint made of worm-eaten wood!"

Poor Lucia went to bed in tears, determined not to go to the Cova the next day. But toward midday on the 13th of July, she was so overcome with longing to go there again that she suddenly jumped up, as if urged by some invisible force, put on her kerchief, and ran to the Marto's house.

She found the two children in their room crying. "You're still here?" she exclaimed, surprised. "But why are you crying?"

"Because you won't come with us and we're afraid to go alone," replied Jacinta sobbing.

"A great number of people have gone to the Cova da Iria," Francisco told her.

"Well, then, it's high time for us to set off," said Lucia.

"Oh, are you coming after all?" stammered Jacinta, drying her tears.

"Yes. I'm coming with you!"

"Oh, everything is all right, then," said the little one, laughing. And the three set off.

When Manuel Pedro saw the children going, he took down his cap from its hook, put it on, and went after them.

❧ 6 ❧

THE GREAT SECRET

Ti Manuel—Uncle Manuel—as Farmer Marto was called by everyone in Aljustrel, rubbed his eyes as he approached the Cova da Iria. Thousands and thousands of people were standing about among the oak and olive trees on the valley pasturage, which normally was utterly deserted. Most of them had brought umbrellas to protect themselves against the scorching sun. Manuel looked about in vain for the children, who had disappeared in the crowd. To his great surprise he came on his wife and his sister-in-law, who were standing on a little hill, trying to get a view over the valley. Each was holding a lighted candle in her hand to protect herself and the children against diabolical influences.

"Where are the children?" asked the farmer, wiping the sweat from his brow.

"Where do you think they are?" said Maria-Rosa shrugging her shoulders. "Why, they're at their tree, of course! Come up here and you'll see them."

"I must go to them!" said Manuel. And he proceeded to push his way through the human wall.

"He's their father. Let him through!" some people who

recognized him shouted. So he reached the hallowed spot at last. But what was this? A low wall had been built around the little tree to protect it from being damaged by inquisitive people or by grazing animals. The branches of the oak tree had been garlanded with silk ribbons, and a kind of triumphal arch adorned with two lamps and a cross, and made of a few planks of rough wood, had been erected in front of it. Someone had placed a table there, too, to hold flowers and lighted candles.

So there must be many who believe in the apparitions, observed Manuel, and to his own surprise he was glad to note this.

Someone pointed out to him the gallant woman who, with her husband and her three children, had done all this. She was Maria de Rosario Carreira, from Moita, one of the first believers.

Manuel reached the children at last; he stood beside Jacinta and was determined to remain there to the end. A crippled boy sat huddled up on a stone beside Lucia. It was João, Senhora Carreira's son, whom his mother had commended to the girl's special intercession.

The children themselves had experienced plenty of difficulty in reaching their sanctuary. From every side, people pressed around them with requests. A woman from Atouguis wanted them to ask the Mother of God to release from his pain a sick person who was suffering most terribly. The wife of the shoemaker Farzeria, weeping bitterly, told Lucia that her husband had gone to the tavern with the last escudo they had. She did not know what they were to live on now. "Please ask Our Blessed Lady to cure him of his drunkenness," she begged.

The hour was gradually approaching when the sun would be at its height. According to Portuguese time, this would be about half-past one. It was shining down more and more pitilessly on the scorched ground. Just as the sun reached its zenith, a bright light flashed across the sky from the east.

"Shut the umbrellas!" cried Lucia in a loud clear voice.

Suddenly it seemed as though the sun were losing its brilliance. A light breeze blew over the countryside and the air became noticeably cooler. The sky took on a curious golden luster. The thousands present stood still, holding their breath. No one dared to make the slightest movement. Then a faint humming sound became audible. At the same time a silvery white cloud was seen to drift over from the direction of the sun and rest above the garlanded tree.

The three children sank to their knees at the same moment. João, the cripple, who was sitting beside Lucia, tried to do the same, but he was unable to remain upright and toppled over. Farmer Marto helped him back on to his stone.

Once more the children saw the wonderful Lady enveloped in heavenly light. Her eyes rested with a slight expression of reproach on Lucia, who cast down her eyes, ashamed of her doubts.

"Won't you speak to her?" Jacinta whispered to her cousin.

It was as silent as in church at the moment when the priest raises up the Sacred Host. Then the bystanders heard Lucia saying in her clear, far-reaching voice, "We have come, Madam, as you told us to. Please tell us what we are to do."

"Come here on the thirteenth of next month, too," the two girls heard the now familiar voice reply. "You must recite the rosary every day in honor of Our Lady, to obtain peace for the world, and that the war may come to an end. For only through prayer can this happen."

Lucia, remembering all her torturing doubts and all the suffering the three of them had had to endure, asked the Lady to tell them her name, and begged for a visible sign of her presence.

The heavenly being replied: "Continue to come here on the thirteenth of each month and in October I shall tell you who I am and what I want of you. And I shall work a great miracle visible to everyone in order that all may believe."

Overjoyed at this promise, Lucia remembered the requests other people had entrusted to her: "Dear Lady, will you please make the limbs of poor João, who is sitting here beside me, straight again?"

"Prayer and suffering are more valuable than health," came the reply. "He must recite the rosary fervently. But I shall help him to bear his infirmity."

She promised to cure others by Christmas if they did not neglect their prayers. Without mentioning his name, Lucia also asked help for the drunkard. The Lady nodded her consent, then continued to speak: "Sacrifice yourselves for sinners and say often, especially when you make a sacrifice, 'Oh, Jesus, it is for love of You, for the conversion of sinners and in reparation for the offenses committed against the Immaculate Heart of Mary!' "

A few moments later Lucia uttered a loud cry, and Farmer Marto noticed that his children also looked terribly frightened. The children saw the Blessed Virgin spread out her hands. Rays of light came out from them and seemed to penetrate right down into the bowels of the earth. An abyss opened before the horrified eyes of the children. They looked into the eternal fire into which the first fallen angels and all the wicked of the world were burning. They saw the torture of the damned in the consuming yet never-ending suffering of those who are distant from God, and they heard the lamentations of the creatures shut out from His sight.

The children covered their eyes with their hands, all three at the same moment, then looked up again toward the heavenly vision as though entreating help.

"You have just seen hell, where the souls of sinners go," continued the Lady kindly but very sadly. "To save them the Lord wishes to establish in the world the devotion to my Immaculate Heart. If people do what I shall tell you, many souls will be saved and there will be peace. The war will soon end. But if people do not stop offending God, it will not be long before another and even worse one begins. That will be in the reign of Pius XI. When you see the night illuminated by an unknown light, know that it is the great sign which is given you, indicating that His judgment is coming upon the world—that the world is about to be punished by war, famine, and persecution against the Church and the Holy Father.

"In order to stop it, I ask that Russia be dedicated to the Immaculate Heart of Mary and that people go to Holy Communion on the first Saturday of the month in reparation for sin.

"If people do what I shall tell you, Russia will be converted, and there will be peace. Otherwise Russia will spread her errors throughout the world by an impious propaganda, and thereby cause wars and persecutions. Many will be martyred.

"The Holy Father will suffer much; several nations will be wiped out."

Farmer Marto looked anxiously at the two little girls, who appeared to be listening with bated breath. He suspected, as did the thousands of others present, that some special revelation was being made to them. Was it something good or something evil? Nothing could be read from the constantly changing expression of the children's faces.

The heavenly Lady continued her revelations concerning the future. At last she concluded with the comforting promise: "My Immaculate Heart will finally triumph. The world will be consecrated to it. Russia will be converted and there will be an era of peace."

Later she added: "When you say the rosary, say at the end of each decade: 'Oh, my Jesus, forgive us our sins, save us from the fire of hell, lead all souls to Heaven, and help with Your grace those most in need of Your mercy.'"

Suddenly all the people in the valley heard a strange rumbling sound which seemed to come from the depths of the earth. Senhora Carreira's triumphal arch swayed as though it would collapse.

"An earthquake!" cried the thousands turning pale and making the sign of the cross.

After a little while the children rose from their knees and Lucia cried out in a loud voice, pointing to the white cloud which was slowly disappearing toward the east: "She's going away!" Then, after a few moments, she added, "I can't see her any more!"

The people gradually recovered from their bewilderment. Even though the heavenly apparition had been neither seen nor heard by them, most of them were convinced that something supernatural had taken place.

Everyone pressed around the little seers and stormed them with questions. The two girls patiently related what they had seen and heard, and repeated to those who had made requests the replies the Blessed Virgin had given. But nobody was able to induce them to tell what had been revealed to them regarding future events. For they had been instructed to remain silent about these revelations and to tell only Francisco, who again this time had heard nothing.

The crowd surged around the children so roughly that little Jacinta was in danger of being crushed. Her father took her up in his arms and carried her away.

The two mothers were standing some distance away, trembling with fear. Olimpia was crying, with her hands pressed to her eyes. "I can't help it—I'm beginning to believe," she told her sister-in-law on the way home. But Maria-Rosa threw back her head, tightened her thin lips, and said grimly, "Even if everyone else believes, I shan't!"

Meanwhile Manuel Pedro kept repeating again and again to the little girl he was carrying in his arms: "Now I too believe, Jacinta. All my doubts have disappeared today!"

And the child smiled happily at him.

Maria Carreira led her son away from the noisy crowd. "Are you very sad that our dear Lady is not going to cure you?" she asked through her tears.

But the boy shook his head resolutely and replied, "Don't cry, Mother! The Blessed Virgin will help me to bear my suffering. No, I'm really quite contented, and I will say the rosary every day from now on."

⚜ 7 ⚜

MESSAGE FROM HEAVEN
OR A HOAX?

As the three children were minding their sheep on the lonely pasture, Francisco got the girls to tell him over and over again what the Blessed Virgin had revealed to them, and every word became deeply impressed on his mind. Nevertheless, much remained obscure; even Lucia was unable to understand and explain everything.

"Who is Russia who the Blessed Virgin said would have to be converted?" the boy wondered.

"Perhaps she's some woman from Vila Nova de Ourém or Moita or somewhere else, whom we don't know at all," suggested Jacinta.

"But a woman from Moita couldn't spread errors throughout the whole world," objected the boy, puzzled. "And that's what Our Lady said Russia would do."

"I think Russia is a country very far away from Portugal," replied Lucia, "but I don't know any more than that."

"Then it must surely be a very wicked and unholy country," said Francisco, "and we must pray for it a whole lot so that it will be converted. And who can Pius XI be?"

"Perhaps he's a king or an emperor?" suggested Jacinta.

"Or he may be a Pope," said Lucia. "Yes, he's a Pope. That's certain. Father Francisco da Cruz, who sometimes comes to Fatima, told me when he was here several years ago about a Pope Pius who wants all the children in the world to make their First Holy Communion while they're still quite young. And Father Cruz persuaded the priest to allow me to make my First Holy Communion very soon afterward. I was six then."

"I'm nine and Jacinta is seven, and we're not yet allowed to make our First Holy Communion," said Francisco sadly.

"That must be because Dom Marcus, who came here two years ago, is a lot stricter than the parish priest before him," replied Lucia. "He doesn't believe that such little children can understand enough about the great sacrament."

"I understand everything already," said Jacinta. "I know that Our Lord is in the Host and wants to come into my heart."

"You're sure to be allowed to make your First Holy Communion soon," said the cousin consolingly. "Our Lady is certain to see that you do. You can trust her!"

"Then we shall have to become a lot better," said the boy. "Our Lady said that we must pray for sinners and sacrifice ourselves for them. If I only knew how we could do that!"

And all three fell to wondering how they could atone for sinners.

"Mother once told us about a saint who wore a thick coarse rope under his shirt," said Francisco thoughtfully.

"Well, there are plenty of ropes," said his sister eagerly, "so let's do that!"

"I think a rope worn over the bare skin would hurt a lot," said Lucia.

"All the better if it does," cried the boy. "Then the penance will be all the bigger."

They really carried out their purpose. Nobody noticed their self-inflicted torment, for the three of them bravely hid the fact that their penitential belts were hurting them. They became extraordinarily inventive in their desire to do penance and make atonement. They often gave the bread which their mothers had given them either to poor children or to the sheep, and they themselves ate acorns which Francisco picked off the oak trees.

"They taste terribly bitter, so it must be a great sacrifice," said Jacinta.

One day Lucia's mother sent them to a very distant pasture with the sheep. The sun was fierce and the children were perspiring with heat. They longed for a drink of water.

"There's a house over there," said Lucia. "Let's go over and ask for a drink."

They were readily given a jug of water. "You drink first," Lucia invited Francisco. He eagerly took hold of the jug, but suddenly he remembered and said, "No, I don't want to!"

"But why not? Aren't you thirsty any more?"

"I am, but I want to bear the thirst for the conversion of sinners."

"Then you take a drink, Jacinta!"

"I want to do penance, too," said the little girl, shaking her head bravely, although she was nearly faint with thirst.

"Well, then, I won't drink either," said Lucia. "Shall we give the water to the sheep?"

"Oh, that's a good idea. Snowflake must have the first drink," cried Jacinta.

"Yes, Snowflake first," agreed Francisco.

They gave the water to the sheep and then took back the jug to the woman who had given it to them, and thanked her.

"That has done you good, hasn't it?" asked the peasant woman kindly.

"Yes, indeed, Senhora," answered Francisco.

The heat became more and more unbearable. Jacinta got a raging headache and every sound hurt her. She even found the croaking of the frogs in the nearby marsh and the chirping of the grasshoppers painful.

"Ah, Lucia," she pleaded, "do tell the frogs and the grasshoppers to keep quiet. I simply can't bear it any more."

"What? You want to make sacrifices and atonement, and then you can't bear a little bit of croaking from the frogs?" said her brother reproachfully.

At this the little girl smiled through her pain and said bravely, "Yes, of course I can. Let them keep on croaking!" And so she bore without a murmur the torturing discomfort which ceased only when the cool evening came.

There was no need to invent such sacrifices; the children had quite enough to bear as it was. At home they were hardly allowed a moment's peace. People were constantly coming to question them and they had to answer every one of them patiently. Sometimes the constant interrogation was too much for them to face, and when they saw someone coming they hid under the beds or in some such place.

One day, as they were going to church together, two strangers asked them if they knew the children to whom the Mother of God had appeared.

"Oh, yes, we know them well!" replied Francisco promptly.

"Can you tell us where they live?"

"Yes, indeed," replied Jacinta, her black eyes shining mischievously. "Two of them live in the little white house there to the right. Lucia lives on the same side a few houses farther up."

"Thank you, we shall find them easily now."

The three of them laughed secretly at getting rid of the troublesome visitors in this way.

Poor Lucia had the worst time of the three, for her mother still obstinately refused to believe in the apparitions.

"You're fooling everyone with your lies," she said again and again, "but I'll teach you yet to tell the truth." And she often beat her.

Her father too was more irritable than ever. The harvesttime was drawing near, and Antonio declared angrily, "We shall have nothing to harvest on our field in the Cova da Iria this year. All those crazy people have trampled it down. Go to your Blessed Virgin, Lucia, and ask her to get us something to eat! We shall certainly all be going hungry soon!"

The younger brothers and sisters persecuted Lucia with the same kind of reproaches. Only the two elder ones tried to protect her. They suspected the truth and made efforts to soften the parents' hearts, but without the least success. The vexation of it all made Antonio dos Santos go to the tavern more than ever, but he met with annoyance there, too. Some of the peasants who had fields near the place of the apparitions reproached him angrily because the inquisitive crowds had trampled their crops. There was nothing left worth harvesting, they said.

"Who will compensate us for the loss?" one of them shouted at him excitedly. "Look here, Antonio, will you pay for the damage?"

"Why should I pay for it?" growled Antonio. "Was it I who appeared over that silly tree? Tell me, was it I or was it the Blessed Virgin? You can apply to her for compensation, or else summon her to the Court at Vila Nova de Ourém! It would serve her right if she were locked up! Why did she have to appear right beside our beans and peas? I've suffered plenty of damage myself!"

"I too have suffered nothing but annoyance over this business," grumbled Guimarães. "There are a great many people who don't come to the tavern any more since the 13th of July. The shoemaker, who used to be my best customer, never turns up here now. I believe his old woman has driven him crazy. They say he has turned over a new leaf and drinks nothing but water now."

"None of you can see beyond the length of your own noses!" cried the village piper, whom the heat had driven to the tavern once more. "Why don't you set up a booth at the Cova and sell your wine there, Antonio? You could do great business! Hundreds of inquisitive people go there every day now."

"I never thought of that!" replied the innkeeper. "To tell the truth, you old buffoon, your suggestion isn't bad at all!"

"And on the thirteenth of next month you will certainly make more than on three feasts of St. Anthony."

"Yes, but what about us? What shall we sell?" grumbled the aggrieved farmer.

"Your land, of course, you blockhead!" replied the piper, grinning knowingly.

"Our land?"

"Yes, of course! Look here! If this business goes on, Fatima will become a place of pilgrimage just like Lourdes in France. Then a great basilica will be built in the Cova da Iria, and big hotels, and all the rest of it. And how much money do you think you will get for your miserable bean fields then, eh?"

"My word!" said the farmer scratching his head. "That would be good business right enough! Perhaps there's something in this apparition affair after all. Why, you're almost making me believe in it, Luis!"

"It's a pity you can't cash in on it yourself, Luis," said the tavern keeper, grinning. "They'll hardly want a piper in the Cova da Iria. I don't think the people will want to dance the fandango there."

"Who said I can't make something out of it?" said the artful fellow with a wink. "I'll buy a whole sack of rosary beads in Ourém tomorrow and sell them to the pilgrims on the thirteenth of next month. 'Buy my rosary beads, Senhores and Senhoras. Buy my rosary beads and medals! They're guaranteed to have touched the holy miraculous tree of the apparitions!' Now, what do you think? Will that be good business or not?"

"You're really not as daft as you seem!" said the tavern keeper. "Come! Have another glass. On the house this time!"

And so the men went home in much better humor that evening. And from that time onward many of them lost their feeling of hostility toward the apparitions.

Dom Marcus suffered more worry than anyone else. He had never liked writing letters, and now everyone was asking him for news. He even had to write to the Patriarch of Lisbon because the diocesan authorities ordered him to do so. He looked thoroughly bad-tempered when he turned up in Olival on the feast of St. John for the parish festival there.

"You look as though you had drunk a barrel of vinegar," said his uncle, Dom Faustino Ferreira, parish priest of Olival and Archpriest of the Deanery of Ourém, laughing heartily.

"It's this wretched business of the apparitions," grumbled Dom Marcus. "I really don't know what to think about them!"

"You should assert your authority," Dom Joaquim, the parish priest of Santa Catarina da Serra, advised him. "Last Sunday I spoke to my parishioners about it from the pulpit and forbade them to visit the Cova da Iria. There's no doubt but that it's all the devil's work. For as we read in the Bible, the devil sometimes takes the guise of an angel of light."

"Your three little shepherd children are playing a trick on us all, Dom Marcus," said another priest, laughing.

"Have you read what *O Século*, the important daily newspaper of Lisbon, has written about Fatima?" asked the parish priest of Vila Nova de Ourém.

"What have those freethinkers been scribbling this time?" someone else asked.

"One moment. I have the last issue of *O Século* here," said the parish priest opening the paper. "Here, I'll read it out to you. Here's the heading: 'A Message from Heaven or a Hoax?'"

"That's outrageous!" exclaimed the Dean.

"Listen! First the writer describes in detail the events of the thirteenth of July, then he goes on: 'In my opinion it is a question of an extremely artful financial enterprise, the source of which originates in the bowels of the earth.

Some cunning fellow has recently discovered a mineral spring, and under the cloak of religion aims to turn the Serra da Aire into a miraculous shrine like Lourdes. The authorities have doubtless heard this already. If not, let them take our information as a warning.'"

"Could that reporter have thought up anything more stupid?" said Dom Marcus with a bitter laugh. "That's the most flagrant nonsense that has been written about it yet."

"Yes, that's true," admitted Dom Joaquim. "But it's just as nonsensical to believe that the Blessed Virgin herself came down from heaven to tell a few dirty little shepherd children from Fatima that they should say the rosary. That's simply childish!"

"Childlike, not childish!" replied the Archpriest. "When you talk to your little goatherds, do you talk about very learned matters to them?"

"No, of course not!"

"Very well. Our Lady does as you do. She speaks in a way that the children are able to understand. Besides, we don't know anything about the secrets she confided to them."

"But what is the use of revelations if only three little shepherd children know of them?" asked the parish priest of Ourém.

"Assuming that the facts are as stated by the children, God will certainly order them in due course to make known the secret."

"But I cannot understand why the Blessed Virgin should come down from heaven herself for this," insisted the parish priest of Santa Catarina.

"You believe in Mary's Assumption into heaven, do you not?"

"Of course I do!"

"Yet you would not care to permit her to come down again if she wants to?"

"Let us keep to serious discussion!" snapped Dom Joaquim. "Of course she can appear whenever she likes and to whom she likes. But I do not care to think that she should choose to appear to a few ignorant children. Why does she not appear to someone who knows something about theological matters—a parish priest, for instance?"

"Because the parish priest would assuredly confront her with the holy water aspergillum and the Rite of Exorcism!" laughed a pleasant, portly little parish priest from a mountain village. "We're all orthodox believers, it is true, but when anything unusual happens not even the toughest freethinker is as frightened of a miracle as we parish priests are."

"Unfortunately there is no article of Canon Law which prescribes that heaven should ask permission of all the parish priests within a radius of ten miles before a miracle is worked," said a young curate with a gleefully mischievous glance at the parish priest of Santa Catarina.

"I really think we are a little too quick to reject the happenings in Fatima," said Dom Faustino when the laughter had died down. "After all, why should not the Mother of God appear in Fatima just as she did in La Salette or in Lourdes? You think the devil is behind it all. Permit me to say that I think otherwise. In my opinion the devil cannot possibly be interested in making people say the rosary."

"But to make everyone kneel down before him with clasped hands would please the devil very much, as you can deduce from the Gospel story of the Temptation of Christ," retorted Dom Joaquim heatedly.

"He does not have to appear in the form of the Blessed

Virgin for that. Quite enough people throughout the world worship him as it is. Of course I do not wish to anticipate the decision of the Church, which must come in due course, but I am inclined to believe in the authenticity of the apparitions if our colleague from Fatima can assure us that there is no possibility of deliberate deception on the part of the children."

"Yes, deception is quite out of the question," declared Dom Marcus.

"Good. Then we shall leave everything in the hands of God. Only the future will tell what it all means. Until then it is advisable for us to be reticent. But we must also be careful not to condemn something which definitely may be from God. If this is from God, then it is a very great grace, not only for Fatima but for us all, and for all Portugal—for all who need help from above in these times."

The words of the old Archpriest, who had once been imprisoned by the godless Government for his loyalty to the Church, made a great impression. Even Dom Joaquim was at a loss for a reply. Dom Marcus drew his fingers nervously through his thick black hair, and said with a sigh, "I wish someone else was parish priest of Fatima. It's far too great a responsibility for my liking."

"I'm just wondering how long it will be until our 'Plumber' takes action," said the parish priest of Ourém. Everyone knew that he meant Arturo d'Oliveira Santos, the Freemason Prefect of the district, who was nicknamed "*o funilero*," the Plumber, after his trade.

"Fortunately the Plumber has spared me so far," said the parish priest.

It was already getting dark when Dom Marcus arrived back in Fatima on his old bicycle. Bonfires were burning in the church square in honor of the feast of St. John, and young and old were dancing the wildest fandangos as the band played. Obviously his sermon of the Sunday following the feast of St. Anthony had had little effect.

And the Mother of God is supposed to appear in a parish like this! thought the priest bitterly.

Farmer Francisco da Silva, the Mayor of Fatima, was waiting for Dom Marcus in his study. The priest did not look too pleased to see him, for the Mayor was a most indifferent Catholic and was seldom seen in church, even on the great feasts.

"Now then, what can I do for you, Mayor?" asked Dom Marcus brusquely.

"It's an awkward business," declared the Mayor, nervously twiddling his tricorn hat in his hands. "The Prefect in Ourém wants a report about the alleged apparitions. I don't know what to write to him."

"Well, everyone knows what's happening here. Write it to him and add that the parish priest of Fatima does not think much of the matter."

"But that would mean writing a long letter," said the Mayor, looking ruefully at his rough hands. "I was never much good with the pen, so I was wondering if you would write out the report yourself. Then I would only have to sign my name to it."

"All this letter writing is very distasteful to me, too," said the priest, laughing. "No, my friend, you will have to write the letter yourself."

"I was afraid it would be like that. Then I had best go to Ourém and make the report personally."

"Just as you wish, my friend!"

"But the story must be put an end to," said the Mayor,

angered by the refusal of his request. "When will you kindly ban all this hocus-pocus?"

"I would willingly do so if I could."

"Perhaps you think quite differently in your heart," growled the Mayor. "They say the so-called pilgrims leave a fair amount of money in the Cova da Iria."

"If only they would bring it to me! I could use it to repair the church tower; it will fall down on top of our heads one fine day."

"Who knows if you're not making a profit out of the business all the same?" insisted Da Silva offensively.

"Do not be so insolent!" said the priest angrily. "If that is what you think, why do you not have the valley cordoned off by the police?"

"By the police? You know very well I've only one policeman in the district—a shaky old fellow with hardly two teeth in his head."

"Well, you can apply for reinforcements."

"They will come all right, Father. You may be sure of that!" snorted the Mayor stamping out and slamming the door after him.

The music happened to have ceased for a moment as the Mayor was coming down the rectory steps.

"Look, there's our *Regedor!*" laughed Luis, the piper, when he saw him coming. "Has the Mother of God converted you at last, that you've gone to confess to the parish priest?"

"Leave me alone, you confounded hen thief!" roared the Mayor, infuriated at the laughter which was breaking out all around them. "Look out! You will be run in one fine day!"

"Just as you please, Senhor *Regedor!*" cried the buffoon

with a derisive bow. This was a subtle joke, for *Regedor* means Mayor in Portuguese, whereas *Regador* means watering can.

"That's an insult to authority!" cried the Mayor, beside himself with rage because more and more people were coming along to laugh at him. "When I see the Prefect in Ourém tomorrow, I shall inform him of this."

"Yes, a *Regador* has to go to the plumber now and then!" cried the piper triumphantly. "An old watering can has to be soldered sometimes!"

"Now you have insulted the Prefect as well," raged Da Silva in a voice of thunder. "You can be imprisoned for that, in case you don't know! Moreover, you're one of those who are backing up the hoax about the apparitions wherever you go."

Fuming with rage the Mayor made his way through the bawling crowd and hurriedly disappeared.

"You'll be nabbed this time," said the tavern keeper Guimarães, shaking his head. "You'll see, the *Regedor* will manage to have you locked up."

"That wouldn't be so bad as long as I do not have to pay for my insult to authority on the 13th of August," said the musician scratching his head. "If I'm in jail then I'll lose good business with the rosary beads. You know what I mean, old wine-waterer?"

8

THE PLUMBER

The days dragged on slowly, but the Fatima folk had little time to rest or meditate. They were right in the middle of the harvest. And besides they were all waiting with intense excitement for the 13th of August. Shortly before the momentous day, Bernardo, the village constable, came to the Marto's house. He had chosen the middle of the day, as he felt sure Farmer Marto would be at home then. He was puffing and sweating pitiably.

"Now, what brings you to see me, old thief-catcher?" asked Manuel Pedro, laughing. "Are you after some murderer whom you think might be hiding in my henhouse?"

"No, neighbor, the matter concerns yourself!" the constable explained with dignity. "I have to serve a summons on you!"

"On me?"

With an air of importance Bernardo took out a paper.

"Here it is: Farmer Manuel Pedro Marto of Aljustrel, in the parish of Fatima, is hereby summoned to appear before the Prefect of Vila Nova de Ourém, together with his child, on Saturday the 11th of August, at ten o'clock in the morning, for the purpose of being questioned on a certain matter. Nonobservance of this summons is a punishable offense."

"The Plumber must have a touch of sunstroke!" replied Ti Manuel, perplexed.

"I don't own to have heard that remark, Manuel!" protested the constable. "We're becoming very sensitive to insults to authority these times!"

"You seem to have a touch of sunstroke, too!"

"Another insult!" said Bernardo.

"Well, wash it down with a little glass of wine!" said Manuel, laughing. "I need a drink to get over the shock."

Bernardo sipped the wine with relish. "The wine is good. It strengthens the heart and weakens the memory, Ti Manuel!" he said appreciatively. "I've completely forgotten what you've just said!"

"This is the first summons I've had since I was called into military service," said the farmer. "Only that time the words read: 'freshly washed.' Didn't you read out that I was to bring my child with me? Which child? I have eight living and one in the cemetery."

"Of course it refers to the children who allege they have seen the Mother of God."

"Is that on the bit of paper?"

"No, that's not in the official summons," replied the policeman with special emphasis, "but I should think it refers to Francisco and Jacinta."

"It only mentions *a* child here, and what you think does not concern me at all, you wily bloodhound."

"Wily bloodhound—that's another insult!"

"I'm ready to take back the expression. But have another little glass!" Bernardo did not have to be asked twice.

"It's forgotten already!" he said with a grin, putting

down his glass. "So now you know—tomorrow at ten o'clock at the Prefect's. I have to go to your brother-in-law Antonio now, for I have a summons for him, too."

"My God, how is it all going to end?" sighed Olimpia, when Manuel told her about the summons.

"What can be the end of it? It won't cost us our heads, anyway!" said the farmer with a grin.

"Are you taking the children with you?"

"I haven't the least intention of doing so!" declared Manuel.

Antonio dos Santos made a wry face, as if he had taken a bite of pepper, when he heard the summons.

"This is a nice business!" he burst out. "Now, Lucia, you'll have to swallow the soup you've cooked yourself!"

"They'll certainly lock you up in prison!" her brothers and sisters told her. "Perhaps they'll even beat you to death."

"The Prefect may do what he likes with you as long as he makes you give up your lies!" said her mother.

Poor Bernardo had yet another unpleasant journey to make that day. On leaving the Santos', he went to the village piper and said to him, "I'm sorry, Luis, but I have to arrest you!"

"Why is that?" asked Luis, who had almost forgotten his insulting behavior already.

"You know yourself what for—that remark about the watering can and the Plumber," said the policeman, yawning sleepily.

"Could you not at least wait until after the thirteenth?" asked Luis irritably.

"No, that's impossible! But I think they'll let you free soon. They won't shut you up for long."

"Very well, then. Discharge your duty!" replied the piper. "Have you the handcuffs with you?"

"No, I knew you'd come along quietly yourself and not give me any trouble."

"Let's have a drink at Guimarães' first!" suggested the prisoner, and the constable made no objection.

"Now you'll have to sell your rosaries in the prison!" said the innkeeper when Luis told him of the arrest. And he laughed so heartily that the tears rolled down his fat cheeks.

Early the following morning Antonio put his daughter up on the donkey. Ourém was almost a three hours' journey away, so they had to set out in good time. Ti Manuel was not quite ready when they went to fetch him, so while waiting, Lucia ran upstairs to Jacinta who was still in bed.

"I'll get up at once and waken Francisco," the little girl said. "Then we'll go to your well and pray for you until you come back."

"And what will you do if they beat me dead?" asked Lucia, groaning.

"Before they do, you must tell them they must fetch us and kill us, too!"

Just then Lucia's father called in the door, telling her to hurry up, and then the small party set off for the dreaded meeting. They arrived in Ourém in good time and were shown into the Prefect's office.

Senhor d'Oliveira Santos was a man of hardly thirty, with sharp features and a small, well-groomed mustache. He looked hard at the two men and the little girl as they came in.

"So you are the disturbers of the peace in Fatima!" he said.

"Disturbers of the peace—not that I know of!" replied Manuel, surprised.

"Now, you know well what I mean. You are Farmer Marto, are you not? Where's your boy? I gave explicit orders that you were to bring your child with you."

"I have eight children. You should have written more clearly which of them you wished to see."

"You know quite well what it's about. Do you really believe in this humbug?"

"In what humbug?"

"Well then, in the alleged apparitions?"

"They are not humbug. It is something holy which comes from heaven, and I believe in it. Or is that forbidden, perhaps?" Manuel looked with secret pleasure at the dry little man who was sitting at a table in a corner, writing down everything.

"How did you arrive at the idea of spreading such lies in Fatima?" asked the Prefect angrily, turning to Lucia.

"I don't spread any lies, Senhor!" replied Lucia bravely, clutching her rosary beads tightly. "What I said is the truth."

"Well, we'll see about that! What is this secret which the apparition is supposed to have confided to you?"

"I am not permitted to say!"

"Why not?"

"The Blessed Virgin forbade me to tell!"

"Probably because the whole hoax would come out if you did! Now, admit that the parish priest started this whole business!"

"The parish priest?" asked Lucia, amazed. "Oh, no, Senhor, the priest always spoke against it and he doesn't believe me."

"Then it's easy to see the kind of lying child you are when even your parish priest doesn't believe what you say."

Lucia bowed her head in shame and did not reply.

"We'll soon throw some light on this matter!" said the Plumber angrily. "The whole clerical hoax will come to light, and then we shall settle our accounts with certain gentlemen. In any case you're not to go to Cova da Iria any more. Do you understand, Lucia?"

"But I must go there. The Mother of God wishes me to do so."

"So you're not only a liar but disobedient as well. Have you not been taught that you must obey those in authority?"

"Yes, but I know that we must obey God and the Blessed Virgin even more than people."

"You're a brazen brat!" raged the Prefect.

"With all due respect to you, Senhor, you have no right to abuse the child!" said Ti Manuel angrily.

"What's that to you?" asked the Plumber crossly. "Surely it's for the father to make any objection if he wants to. Why don't you open your mouth, Senhor dos Santos?"

"But what can I say, Senhor?" replied the farmer, bewildered. "This business has been bothering me for a long time. I have nothing at all to do with it really. Only my daughter can tell you anything about it!"

"Haven't you asked enough questions?" asked Manuel. "We're right in the middle of the harvest and haven't time to spend palavering in offices, telling you the same things a hundred times over."

"Go to the devil!" cried the Prefect. "We shall see what's to be done about this matter. You will be hearing from me again!"

"Well, I suppose we can go now!" said Manuel good-humoredly. "Come along, Antonio!" As they left the office Farmer Marto turned toward the dry little clerk who was just then squirting the ink out of his fountain pen, and said with a derisive grin: "Well, little man, have you been able to get it all down?"

The secretary stared disconcertedly at the farmer and stammered, "Yes, of course, I have written down everything!"

"Clear out of here!" thundered the Prefect.

"With the greatest pleasure!" replied Manuel. On the way home he chuckled now and then. "When I think of the look on that scribbler's face!" he said. "It was well worth the long journey to Ourém to see it."

"I cannot see anything funny in the whole business," muttered his brother-in-law.

In the meantime the two Marto children were sitting in the Santos' garden by the draw well, one of their favorite haunts, saying one rosary after another for Lucia. After a long time Catarina dos Santos came to draw water.

"Have you heard anything of Lucia yet?" asked Francisco anxiously.

"Oh, yes, they have just beaten her to death," replied the girl indifferently.

"Beaten her to death!" exclaimed the boy turning pale.

"Yes, of course! They telephoned the news to the Mayor. That's what happens to people who spread such lies."

"Then we'll go to Ourém and let them beat us to death, too!" said Jacinta. But she was unable to keep back her tears.

"Let us say another rosary first!" suggested the boy as Catarina went away with her pitcher on her head.

The children were still absorbed in their prayers when they suddenly heard someone calling them.

"It's you, Lucia!" cried Jacinta, jumping up and running to her cousin. "But Catarina has just told us that they had beaten you to death!"

"So you see who tells lies here!" muttered Francisco angrily.

"Yes, I'm here again!" said Lucia, laughing and embracing the little girl. "They didn't do anything to me. The Prefect only scolded, but Ti Manuel stood up for me splendidly!"

"And the Blessed Virgin protected you. So you see there's nothing for us to be afraid of."

The next day, which was the 12th of August, the three children were playing blindman's buff with some other boys and girls when the first pilgrims arrived.

"How can children who have seen the Mother of God play blindman's buff?" asked a lady indignantly. She was a pilgrim from a distant town.

"It just shows how natural and childlike the little seers are!" said a gentleman who was with her. "I take that as a good sign."

But alas the game soon had to stop because more and more people came along. They asked question after question, took the children aside, and confided to them all kinds of intentions which they were to convey to the Mother of God.

"But how can we remember them all?" asked Lucia anxiously.

Soon the village street was packed with people on foot, on donkeys and in horse carts, and there were even some in automobiles, too. There were also some priests among the crowd, and the children were astonished to observe that these were among the most unbelieving. The parents finally had to take their children home by force, otherwise they would have been pestered all night long.

By the morning the crowd was ten times larger. The article which had appeared in the Freemasons' paper *O Século* had spread the news of the happenings in Fatima throughout the country. So it was not only the pious and the curious from the neighboring villages who came that day; people also came from Lisbon and Coimbra and Porto and almost every town in Portugal. The children had taken their sheep to Valinhos early in the morning, but the pilgrims found them even there and gave them no peace.

About ten o'clock Teresa Marto came running to them, quite out of breath. "Come quick!" she cried. "The Prefect is here and wants to speak to you."

"The Prefect!" stammered Lucia, pressing her hands to her heart.

"Yes, he came in a horse trap. There's a priest with him."

"Then it won't be so bad!" declared Francisco bravely.

When they arrived home they found the man they feared so much conversing intimately with a priest. It was Dom Manuel, the parish priest of Pôrto de Mos, one of the priests who did not believe in the apparitions and was determined to put an end to the "wanton game."

The Plumber's attitude was quite different today. "I've come to see the miracle!" he said in an almost friendly manner. "Yes—just like St. Thomas—to see and to believe!"

"You do right," agreed Lucia eagerly.

"You see, he's not so bad after all!" Jacinta whispered to her brother.

But Francisco answered doubtfully, "I don't know; I don't trust him."

"But after all there's a priest with him."

Just at that moment Farmer Marto came in. He had been called from the fields. "What's going on here?" he asked suspiciously.

"We have come with the very best intentions!" declared the priest. "This matter is so important that we want to question the children closely once more. One cannot do enough to get at the truth."

"Then get at the truth, Father!" replied Manuel in a surly tone.

"Very well, we will take the children with us to the parish priest and question them in his presence."

"As far as I'm concerned, you may do that, but I shall take them there myself."

Antonio dos Santos was also called in to see the visitors, and after some hesitation he too decided to go with the children. This questioning took place on the open veranda of the rectory overlooking the church square. Many of the villagers and pilgrims crowded around the rectory, looking on, some with curiosity, others with unconcealed mistrust. The Prefect asked Dom Marcus to start the examination.

"You know that it is a sin to tell lies," said Dom Marcus, "and anyone who tells lies in such an important matter as this certainly commits a mortal sin and will go to hell if he does not revoke what he has said."

"Yes, I know that!" said Lucia. "But I don't tell lies. I only tell you what we have seen and heard."

"Is it true that the Lady confided a secret to you?"

"Yes, but I may not tell it. But if you want to know it, Father, I shall ask the Blessed Virgin for permission to tell you."

So the cross-examination continued in the same way as on all the other occasions. At last the Prefect looked at the clock and said, "It is time to go to the Cova. I hope you will allow me to take the children there in my car," he said turning to the fathers. "There are such crowds that I'm afraid they might crush the children to death. We shall drive to the Cova by a roundabout way."

"Very well, that's all right," agreed Manuel.

The Prefect took leave of the priest, smilingly helped the children into the gig, took up the reins, and drove off.

"Where is he taking them to?" asked the people pressing around the two fathers.

"He's taking them by a roundabout way to the Cova so that you don't crush them to pulp," replied Manuel Pedro. This reassured the people, and they hurried off to the valley.

There was an enormous crowd in the Cova da Iria—between fifteen and twenty thousand people. Guimarães the tavern keeper, who had set up a booth, did good business because of the terrible heat, and so did a large number of little traders who were selling fruit and other refreshments. There was no doubt but that most of the people present believed, and they said the rosary aloud. But there was a small minority of the people who did not conceal their doubt.

The tree of the apparition was now just a miserable stump, for all the branches had been pulled off it. What remained was decorated with flowers and silken ribbons. There were many candles standing on a table, ready to be lighted the moment the apparition appeared. Even Maria dos Santos, Lucia's eldest sister, had put a candlestick there; she no longer had any doubts.

Midday approached, but there was still no sign of the children. The crowd became more and more restless. Those who had been in the church square earlier reported that the

Plumber had driven off with the children and had surely kidnapped them.

"The parish priest must be in it!" someone cried.

"And the *Regedor* of Fatima, too! Else what made him slink along to the rectory on the feast of St. John?"

The crowd became furiously indignant; threats and abusive words were heard. Some Fatima folk, who had been reviling the children only a short time before, were now their staunchest defenders. Suddenly a peal of thunder was heard in the midst of the ever-increasing tumult.

"A thunderstorm!" cried some.

"No, it must have been a bomb!" cried others.

There was a terrible uproar; children cried and clung to their mothers; women fainted.

"Be quiet, folks!" cried Farmer Marto. "Keep calm! Nothing bad is happening." But he could not make his voice heard above the tumult.

At that moment a brilliant flash of lightning crossed the sky. At once the uproar died down. Everyone stared as if spellbound at the little white cloud which drifted slowly along from the east and then remained stationary above the leafless evergreen oak. Meanwhile the sun had lost its glaring brightness, but an extraordinary array of colored light fell down on the Cova da Iria. Red, blue and golden rays were cast on the grass and the trees, and the people's clothes and faces. The crowd stood breathless staring at the feathery cloud which remained stationary over the miracle tree for about ten minutes, then it rose into the sky again and moved away toward the east.

"A miracle! A miracle!" cried thousands of voices. "The Mother of God came and the children were not there! My God, forgive us our sins!"

Thousands of people fell to their knees, sobbing. Others

urgently pushed their way toward the oak tree and attempted to touch it.

"We will build a chapel in honor of the Blessed Virgin!" a few people cried. Coins and notes began to pile up on the table with the candles.

"What's to be done with this?" asked Maria Carreira, who this time also had taken the lead in decorating the place.

"Take it in trust for us and build a chapel with it!" they shouted. "We'll bring more, a lot more!"

It was quite awhile before the crowds dispersed. Some people hurried to the rectory, uttering threats.

"Where have you had the children carried off to?" they shouted up toward the rectory, but the priest did not dare to show his face. Manuel Pedro had all he could do to squeeze his way through the crowd and get up the steps.

"Go home, folks!" he cried in a loud voice. "I was there, and the parish priest had nothing to do with it. Have confidence! Our Blessed Lady will bring the children home again!"

But the raging crowd refused to break up for a long time after that.

Meanwhile Senhora Olimpia was standing outside her house with her sister-in-law, listening horror-stricken to all the noise which reached Aljustrel from the faraway Cova and from the church square. At last some people came and told them excitedly that the Prefect had carried off the children.

"Oh, my God, what is he going to do with them?" lamented Olimpia.

But her sister-in-law, who still remained unbelieving, laughed bitterly. "Do you think he's going to eat them?

Why do they persist with their lies, making fools of everyone?" she asked.

"No, no, they are not telling lies!" declared Senhora Marto. "I believe, too; I believe in the miracle of the Cova da Iria!"

"And I tell you it's all lies!" replied Maria-Rosa unmoved.

"Antonio!" cried Olimpia to her eldest son, who had just returned from the Cova. "The Prefect has carried off the children. What shall we do?"

"I'll go and look for them!" said the young peasant, and he got onto his bicycle and rode off. Toward evening he returned and reported that he had seen the children on the veranda of the Plumber's house. They did not look as if they had suffered any harm.

"Thank God!" cried the mother. "If only they come home again safe and sound."

"You have no cause to worry so much!" said Manuel Pedro. "The Mother of God will look after them. Besides, the Plumber would not dare to do anything to them."

❧ 9 ❧

IN THE PRISON OF OURÉM

"Stop! Where are you driving to?" cried Francisco when the Prefect turned left off the high street. "To get to Cova da Iria you should turn right!"

"We have to pick up another priest!" the Plumber told them. But the farther on they drove the more uneasy the children became.

"We'll arrive too late, it's almost midday!" lamented Lucia. "Please turn back!"

"Hold your tongues!" said the Prefect angrily. "You'll soon see where I'm taking you to."

The children reluctantly submitted to their fate and began to say the rosary. It was long past midday when the horse trap drew up in front of the Plumber's house.

"Come in here with me!" the Plumber ordered them. He then took them into a room which he locked from the outside.

"What shall we do?" lamented Lucia. "The hour for the Blessed Virgin to appear is already past."

"The Blessed Virgin knows we're here," Jacinta reassured her, "and we'll see her again on the 13th of September."

"But it's a long time until then!" said the boy sadly.

The Prefect's wife came in with a meal for the children. "Now have something to eat!" she said kindly. "You must be very hungry."

"We want to go home!" begged Lucia.

"Oh, you'll get home again all right!" the woman assured them. "No harm will come to you." In her heart she condemned the unworthy trick which her husband had played on the children. She herself was a good Catholic and had had all of her children baptized secretly without his knowledge.

"Do you know who she makes me think of?" said Francisco when they were alone again. "She makes me think of Pontius Pilate's wife. She was good, too, and she did not want her husband to condemn Our Lord."

They ate their meal without much enthusiasm. At last the Plumber returned and said, "You may go home now if you first tell me the secret."

"We must not do that!" replied Lucia resolutely.

"Very well, then, you will have to stay here until you decide otherwise!" declared the Prefect, going out and locking the door behind him.

His wife, who felt sorry for the children, looked in at them every now and then. "Come, let us go out on the veranda," she said one time. "You need some fresh air, and it's cool and shady out there now."

When they got outdoors, the three little children looked longingly up at the sky as if they expected to see the Mother of God.

"Hi, Francisco! Jacinta!" they suddenly heard. And to their great joy they saw down below their brother Antonio, who was just getting off his bicycle. They waved at him merrily, but they could not speak to him as the Prefect came along just then, took them back to the room and locked them in. In the evening the wife brought them a little meal again and left them pillows and blankets for the night.

"Shall we break away?" Francisco whispered to the girls. "We could open the window, and it's not very far to the ground."

"No, we'll stay here!" Lucia decided. "They won't keep us locked up forever."

The following morning the cross-examination began once more, but it was all in vain. Neither promises nor threats would make the children tell the secret.

"Very well, then, you have to go to prison!" decided the Prefect, shutting his portfolio.

The children were led away by a policeman as if they were criminals. The passers-by stared, astonished, at the strange spectacle.

"What on earth can little scamps like those have done to be locked up?" they asked each other.

"Ah, they must have stolen. The world is becoming worse and worse!" others said, shrugging their shoulders and going their way.

The Prefect, who wanted to give the children a thoroughly good fright, had them sent to a big cell where there were about a dozen other prisoners.

"You shall stay here until you do what the Prefect tells you!" said the policeman grimly. And he locked the door with a great rattle of keys.

"Now, what have you been up to?" a big ragged fellow with a scarred face asked the terrified children, who were clinging close together.

"They must have stolen!" chuckled another, sitting up slowly on his bundle of straw.

"They're beginning young with the light fingers!" crowed a bald-headed convict with a face like a vulture.

"Was it worthwhile?" asked another.

"What did you pinch? Are you pickpockets, eh?"

"They should lock up your parents for putting you to thieving so young!" muttered another.

The children stared bewildered at the rough faces around them.

"You seem to have lost your tongues!" laughed the giant.

"But we haven't stolen anything, Senhor!" protested Francisco, taking courage.

"There are no 'Senhores' here!" said the man with the vulture's face. "But I suppose you're shy. Very well, then, we'd better introduce ourselves. See, this tall chap here is a murderer. He killed his wife with a knife because she let the soup burn. That young pup over there poisoned his aunt. This fellow here stole a box of gold; and this one has a couple of dozen acts of perjury on his conscience. That man there threw an innocent child into the water; and this one here set fire to half a town." Then he pointed to a prisoner who was lying on a sack of straw with his face to the wall, snoring. "That man shot the Emperor of China dead with moth balls," he said. "Hi, wake up, neighbor! We have visitors!"

"What's the matter with you, waking me up from a beautiful sleep?" said the man, yawning. "I was dreaming of a big roast goose, and just as I was swallowing the first bite the fellow wakes me up. But who's here?" he continued, staring at the children.

"Oh, Luis, Luis!" cried Jacinta running over to him. "How good that you're here!"

*Jacinta and Francisco Marto, and Lucia dos Santos,
the children who saw Our Lady of the Rosary*

An artist's conception of the apparition of Our Lady

The village square at Fatima

Pilgrims march toward the shrine, unmindful of the hot sun

Lucia dos Santos, only surviving member of the Fatima children

Pilgrims washing in the pool

A procession during the Holy Year of 1950

A little shepherdess watches her flock today

"Well, I really don't find it so good!" said the village piper, laughing, as he sat up. "But what on earth brings you here?"

"They've probably been pinching!" said the giant, grinning.

"We haven't done anything wicked!" protested Francisco.

"The Prefect locked us up because we wouldn't tell him the secret of the Cova da Iria."

"How long have you been away from home?"

"Since yesterday morning!" Lucia told him.

"The Prefect was in Fatima and promised to take us to the Cova in his horse trap, but he carried us off to Ourém instead."

"Then you have missed the time for the apparition?"

"Alas, yes!" said Jacinta with a sigh.

The piper laughed uproariously. "So I really haven't missed anything!" he cried, still laughing. "But the Plumber will be disappointed yet. Just wait and see! On the 13th of September half of Portugal will come to the Cova."

"Tell me, are all these really murderers and robbers and people who have set fire to places?" whispered Jacinta timidly.

"Ah, what are you saying! Why, they're quite harmless rascals. That one pinched someone else's hen by mistake; the one over there is a tramp and he begged. And that one with the bird's face sold matches and shoelaces without a license. The boy over there did a bit of smuggling. There's definitely no murderer or robber among us, and when the fellows have washed and had a shave again they won't look half bad."

"But why did they lock you up?" Francisco asked.

"Ah, it was really only because I mixed up two letters of

the alphabet! I called our *Regedor* a *Regador*. That was all."

"That's funny!" said Francisco, laughing, for he had now lost all his fear. "The Mayor really does look like a watering can with his long nose."

"Well, now you know the sort of people you're locked up with!" said the giant, joining the conversation again. "The most respectable people are in prison. The real criminals are not caught at all. But now let us hear what you have been run in for."

"You said something about an apparition just now, Luis!" said the man with the vulture's face. "These couldn't, by any chance, be the children to whom the Virgin Mary appeared?"

"Yes, that they are!" replied Luis. "And because the Blessed Virgin was to come again yesterday, that confounded Plumber locked up the children."

"Don't curse like that, Luis!" Francisco warned him. "You know it's a sin!"

"You're right!" replied the piper. Then, turning to his fellow prisoners he said, "Listen, you jailbirds! If any one of you curses or speaks a word not fit to be said in the presence of these children, I'll wring his neck!"

"Don't get so worked up!" muttered the giant. "We know ourselves what's proper."

"I suppose you're feeling real sad now," said the piper, "but cheer up! The Plumber will send you home again soon. If he doesn't, it will be the worse for him. Do you know what? I'll play you a merry fandango!"

Saying this he pulled his mouth organ out of his pocket and began to play a lively tune. The prisoners squatted around the children in a circle and clapped their hands in time to the music, just as the people do at village festivals.

The children too sat down and listened with pleasure. After a while Jacinta could not keep still any longer. She jumped up and began whirling round gracefully and rapidly, snapping her fingers as she danced. The tune became quicker and quicker, and Jacinta whirled around in a circle at great speed. The prisoners looked on, beaming with pleasure and applauding. They were so absorbed in the children that they did not notice the door being unlocked and a warder coming in.

"You're having a jolly time here!" he snorted after he had watched the dancing for a moment.

Jacinta suddenly stopped abashed, then fled to her companions.

"And these are the children who are supposed to have seen the Mother of God!" said the warder shaking his head. "Well, you needn't be afraid, I won't do you any harm!" he added good-humoredly, noticing the children's frightened faces. "You can go on with it, but don't make so much noise!" With this he shuffled off, locking the door behind him. "Imagine putting innocent little creatures like those into a prison with rascals!" he muttered sadly as he went away. He himself had a couple of children the same age as the little ones, and he was very indignant over what the Prefect had done.

"Now we want to hear the exact story of the apparitions," the man with the vulture's face demanded.

Lucia told everything, and as she spoke she completely forgot where she was. Her face became quite beautiful and a strange light shone from her eyes. When she had finished, the men remained silent for a long time.

"I don't think they're telling lies!" said the giant at last. All the rascals and tramps, who were used to being pretty badly knocked about in life and knew nothing but squalor and misery, felt as if something quite unusual had entered the cell, something supernatural and angelic. They sat quite silent, looking in front of them.

"It's many a long day since I said the 'Our Father,' " the vulture-faced man said at last with a sigh.

"Then let us begin right now!" cried Lucia eagerly.

"Yes, we'll all say the rosary together!" agreed Jacinta. She took a little medal of Our Lady from around her neck and asked one of the men to hang it on a nail which she discovered between the cobwebs on the whitewashed wall. Then the children knelt down. The men looked at each other, embarrassed. Then one after another they got up and sank down heavily on their knees.

"Wait a minute!" said Francisco, interrupting the prayers. Then he whispered reproachfully to the giant, "You've still got your hat on!"

The man quickly pulled the big sombrero from his head and threw it on the ground beside him. Lucia began again, and the rough fellows clasped their hands and answered the prayers as if they were kneeling in church. When they were saying the last decade, the door creaked again. The warder walked in and looked in astonishment at the strange spectacle. Then he too took off his cap and fell on his knees.

"To tell the truth, up to now I've only pretended to believe because I thought I'd do a bit of good business as a result of it!" admitted Luis when they had finished the last Hail Mary. "But now, after saying the rosary, I believe the apparition is true!" The other prisoners nodded silently.

Even the warder was touched. Then he said with a laugh: "Dancing and praying—they go together with you, eh? But come along with me now, children. You're to see the Prefect again."

The children said good-by to the prisoners and left the cell with the warder.

"Well, have you thought it over?" asked the Plumber when they were led into his office by a policeman.

"We cannot say anything more than we have said already!" replied Lucia resolutely.

"In that case we'll put an end to the business!" thundered the brutal fellow. "You're going to be put into a pot of boiling oil if you do not tell me what I want to know. Is the pot of oil already on the fire?" he asked the policeman.

"Yes, it will soon be boiling!" replied the policeman.

"So we shan't have long to wait!" The Prefect took the children to another room. "Stay here until someone comes for you!" he said, and locked the door behind him. The children, terrified by all the threats, were quite certain that the Plumber was going to kill them.

Jacinta began to cry.

"Why are you crying?" her brother asked. "Aren't you ready to offer your life for the conversion of sinners?"

"Oh, yes!" sobbed the little girl. "I'm only crying because we won't see Father and Mother again before we die."

"We'll see them again in heaven!" said Lucia consolingly.

"I'm not crying any more!" said Jacinta, though the tears were still flowing down her cheeks.

Just then the Prefect came back. "Will you speak now?" he bellowed.

"We have nothing to say except what we have said a hundred times!" declared Lucia.

"And what about you?" asked the man turning to Jacinta. "Have you nothing to say either?"

"No!" replied the child, trying to speak resolutely.

"My patience is exhausted! Throw her into the cauldron!" the Prefect ordered. The policeman took the girl by the arm and dragged her out of the room. Jacinta had hardly time to give a look of farewell to the others.

"Good-by until we meet in heaven!" her brother called after her. Then he began to pray in a low voice.

"What are you mumbling there?" snapped the Prefect.

"I'm praying that my sister won't be frightened."

After a while the policeman came back to the room. "That one is dead," he announced. "Which of them is next?"

"Tell me the secret, Francisco!" demanded the Prefect.

"I cannot! I really cannot!" Francisco blurted out.

"Throw him into the cauldron!" thundered the Prefect, and the boy, too, was taken out of the room.

"Now you see what has happened to your companions," he said, turning to Lucia. "You're a sensible girl, not as stupid as the others. Will you tell me what I want to know?"

"I have nothing to say!" gasped the girl, beginning to pray again.

"Then throw her into the cauldron, too!" Oliveira Santos ordered the policeman, who had just returned.

"In the name of God!" replied Lucia following him out without faltering. To her great surprise she found Francisco and Jacinta in the room to which the policeman took her.

"Don't rejoice too soon!" said the policeman threateningly. "The oil wasn't hot enough yet. You'll soon be thrown into the cauldron all together." And saying this he slammed the door behind him.

"I don't think they're going to kill us at all now!" Francisco whispered. "It's really a pity, because then we'd go straight to heaven as martyrs."

"Yes, it really is a pity!" said Jacinta.

"Perhaps they will kill us after all!" said Lucia.

Toward evening they were taken back to the Plumber's house, where they had spent the previous night. The Prefect was at his wit's end.

"I've never come across such obstinacy in all my life!" he growled as he sat at breakfast with his wife the following morning.

"I beg of you to give up the cruel game!" his wife pleaded. "Take the children home again!"

"There's nothing else I can do!" he replied angrily. "The Mayor of Fatima telephoned me last evening. There's the devil of a row going on there. He says there are many people who are determined to free the children by force. The business could easily turn out badly for me."

In Fatima there was High Mass in honor of the Assumption of Our Blessed Lady. During the sermon most of the congregation sat with bowed heads, staring grimly in front of them. After Mass the people surged around Farmer Marto in the church square and asked him about the children. He shook his head sadly. They had not yet returned home. As the parish priest went to his house he met with many black looks, and several men and boys shook their fists and flourished sticks at him.

But suddenly a woman shouted, "There are the children! Look, on the veranda! Don't you see them?"

"Father! Father!" cried Francisco and Jacinta joyfully when they caught sight of Manuel. He ran quickly up the steps and took the children in his arms.

Now the Prefect himself came out on the veranda. "You

see, the children have come to no harm," he said. "They can go to the Cova da Iria as often as they wish in the future! Calm yourselves, people! It was only a misunderstanding!"

In spite of these words the anger of the crowd became more and more apparent. Manuel was afraid that the excited people might storm the rectory. So he called out in a loud voice:

"Listen to me, people! Some of you are shouting against the parish priest, others against the *Regedor*, and others against the Prefect. Lack of faith is the cause of all the trouble. What has happened has been permitted by God. Only He knows why."

Now even the parish priest found courage to show himself. "Quite right, Senhor Manuel! Quite right!" he cried in a loud voice.

In spite of all this, the Prefect was not feeling very safe. So the sly fox turned in a friendly way to Manuel and said, "We need a glass of wine after all the excitement! May I invite you to drink one with me, Senhor Marto?"

The good-natured Manuel thought the people would be more likely to calm down if he went off with the Prefect in a friendly manner. And that's how it turned out. When the people saw the two of them going into the nearby tavern apparently on the best of terms, they calmed down and dispersed. When the noise had subsided Dom Marcus sat down with a sigh of relief.

"It would not have taken much more to make the people of Fatima kill their own parish priest!" he said. "And yet a few days ago these same people were threatening the three children, for whom it seems they would now let themselves be torn to pieces."

But in spite of all the signs from heaven, he himself was still unable to believe in the miracle. For a long time he sat staring sadly in front of him, overwhelmed with the grief of a priest who has become lonely in his own parish because the souls entrusted to his care have lost confidence in him. At last he came to a decision. He wrote a statement declaring on his honor as a priest that he had known nothing of the plan to carry off the children, and strongly condemning the action.

A few days later this declaration appeared in *A Ordem*, the only Catholic newspaper in Lisbon. Many were satisfied with this assurance. Others shook their heads and said, "He who excuses himself, accuses himself." Even some of his priestly colleagues thought it would have been better had Dom Marcus remained silent.

The Freemason papers, and above all the Lisbon paper *O Mundo*, were foaming with rage about the events in Fatima and the obvious defeat of their cause. They wrote of nothing but "clerical plots, wicked swindles and wanton exploitation of the religious feelings of the faithful," and they demanded that the swindlers should be hounded down and punished.

But if the parish priest of Fatima did not act very wisely, the writers in the liberal papers served their own cause even less cleverly. The only result of their campaign was that people were now discussing the apparitions in the Cova da Iria all over the country.

The Plumber too drove home feeling anxious and thoughtful. Through his wicked trick he had achieved just the opposite result to the one he had intended. He had actually caused many to believe in the apparitions.

"Dear friend!" a kindred spirit said to him when he returned home to Ourém, "if Fatima really becomes the Lourdes of Portugal, then it is thanks to you."

Arturo d'Oliveira Santos shrugged his shoulders and became immersed in gloom. After a time he suddenly thought of a means of giving what he hoped would be the death blow to the story of the miraculous apparitions in Fatima.

❧ 10 ❧

ONE ORATOR AND A HUNDRED DONKEYS

The following Saturday Farmer José Cardosa trotted peacefully through the streets of Fatima on his donkey. He had brought a sack of corn to the mill, and, as it was a scorching day, he was just thinking of going to have a pint in Guimarães' when a strange fellow came up to him and pushed a red printed note into his hand. Shaking his head the peasant twisted and turned the paper in his hands, but since he could not read he did not know what to do with it. So he stuck it into his pocket and continued on his way. When he got to the tavern he tied his donkey outside, and, wiping the sweat from his forehead, went in.

The bar was full of local people and farmers from the neighboring villages. They were all talking excitedly, and each of them had the same kind of little note in his hand.

"What's written on the note?" asked José when he had ordered his pint.

"One of you read it out!" cried someone else, who was also looking at the bit of paper helplessly. "Come on, Carlos, you know how to read!"

"Well, listen here!" said Carlos, a cattle dealer from

Fatima. He cleared his throat with an air of importance and read:

"To all Friends of Freedom!

"For some months past certain thoughtless and criminal re-actionaries in Fatima have been staging a spectacle which is an insult to the intelligence of every rational person. The alleged apparitions of the Virgin Mary are no doubt a stratagem put up by clerical circles and Jesuits in disguise. Friends of Freedom! How much longer are you going to tolerate this unworthy comedy staged by clerics as a cloak for their greed and lust for power?

"Freedom-loving citizens of the Serra de Aire! We call upon you to unmask these unscrupulous swindlers and show up all the reactionary elements of Fatima!

"On Sunday the 19th of August we shall all meet in the church square of Fatima and go in procession to the Cova da Iria. There, Senhor José do Vale, Editor of the important daily paper *O Mundo,* will give a rousing address of protest.

"Friends of Freedom! Come in large numbers!

The Committee of Action."

"What does the writer call us, Carlos?" asked a Fatima farmer indignantly. "Read it out again!"

"Reactionary elements he calls us!" repeated the cattle dealer grinning.

"I don't really know what 'reactionary element' means," cried the farmer, "but it is sure to be something insulting. We won't let ourselves be called reactionary elements. Am I not right?"

"Of course you're right!" they cried from all sides.

"We won't put up with such abuse!"

"And especially not from a pen pusher like that from the town!"

"We will all bring thick cudgels or flails with us and drive every one of those city toffs from our village!" suggested a miller's boy, looking with satisfaction at his brawny arms.

"The best thing would be for no one to turn up at all!" said the tavern keeper. "That's what will annoy the fellows most of all."

"But they've chosen the exact time when the High Mass is finished! The church square is full of people then."

"The parish priest should say Mass somewhere else tomorrow!" one of the men suggested. "Come and let us talk to him about it!"

"I have an idea!" said José Cardosa chuckling and rubbing his hands together. "Tell me, how many of you have a donkey?"

"I have a donkey!" replied a farmer.

"I have one, too! I have one, too! Nearly every one of us has a donkey!"

"Well, now listen to me!"

That evening the "reactionary elements" went home looking very well pleased with themselves.

The following morning a car bearing a Lisbon license plate drove noisily into the church square of Fatima.

"Look, there's not a soul to be seen!" cried José do Vale, the editor, a thin little man with large spectacles.

"They're still stuck in the church with their priest!" conjectured Arturo d'Oliveira Santos, who had hatched the whole plan. "But there's the Mayor of Fatima himself! I say, Senhor da Silva, how long will it be until the Mass is over?" he called to the *Regedor*.

"Yes, this is an awkward business," explained the *Regedor*, obviously embarrassed. "The parish priest is not celebrating the High Mass at Fatima today, but at Ortiga, two kilometers away. The church here is locked."

"Confound it!" growled the editor. "I could have spared

myself the long journey to this dirty peasants' hole. The entire plan seems to have misfired completely. Did you not have the leaflets distributed in good time among the people, Prefect?"

"Of course I did! Numbers of them were distributed yesterday in Fatima and in all the outlying villages."

"Well, I simply don't understand at all! Or perhaps you could explain it to me, *Regedor?*"

"Maybe the leaflet might have been better worded!" said the Mayor, scratching himself behind the ear. "The allusion to the reactionary elements in Fatima annoyed a lot of people. Besides, nearly everyone in the village believes in the apparitions."

"That just shows what a backward lot they are!" declared the Plumber, who was angry at the criticism of his bungled effort.

"Everything seems to turn out badly in this business!" snapped the editor.

"Here come a few people!" cried the Mayor with an air of relief as he saw half a dozen young fellows from other villages sauntering along.

"Well, let us drive to that accursed Cova da Iria!" said the Freemason from Lisbon. "Perhaps they're waiting for us there! Get in, *Regedor!*"

The old automobile rattled along, emitting exhaust fumes, while the youths trotted behind it.

A strange sight met their eyes in the Cova da Iria. Near the tree of the apparition a huge load of hay had been piled up, and a donkey had been tied to each of the nearby trees. They were all braying miserably, trying to get to the hay which they could not reach. The little farmer José Cardosa and a few of his companions had hidden themselves in the vicinity, and they burst out laughing when they saw the disappointed faces of the Freemasons.

"Someone has taken the liberty of playing an abominable joke on us!" roared the editor, crimson with rage.

"There are certainly asses from other parts here, too!" said the *Regedor*, rising to the defense of his village.

"But most of the asses definitely belong to Fatima! How could it be otherwise in such a backward hole, full of idiots!"

The Mayor looked hurt but said nothing.

Reluctant to go away without having accomplished their goal, the party waited for quite a time before they could make up their minds what to do.

Meanwhile, Mass was over in Ortiga and many of the congregation made their way to the Cova, curious to know what was taking place there.

"Well, now you have a big enough audience!" said the Prefect, relieved.

The people laughed when they saw the gentlemen surrounded only by donkeys, which kept on braying piteously.

"Why haven't you started yet?" someone called out ironically to the Freemasons. "You see how eager the donkeys are to hear you!"

"Arrest the fellow!" the editor ordered Bernardo, the village constable, who came hurrying along with his sword dangling by his side.

"I don't know him! He's not from these parts!" declared Bernardo, who was bathed in perspiration.

"Well, you can at least ask him his name!" said the Prefect severely.

"I'm the Tsar of Russia!" jeered the fellow.

"I don't believe he's the Tsar of Russia!" declared the

policeman, disconcerted, while the man disappeared in the crowd.

"Well, won't you begin, Senhor!" the Plumber urged the editor.

"Yes, that will be best!" said the *Regedor*.

Senhor do Vale stood up on a seat of the open car and began to deliver his well-prepared speech about the outrageous hoax of which devout people in Fatima and all over Portugal were the victims. The people listened for a while, grinning. But when, carried away by his own eloquence, he used the unfortunate term, "reactionary elements," the listeners lost patience.

"What's this? Does the fellow want to insult us in our own village?" someone interrupted.

"We'll just show you what kind of reactionary elements we are!" cried others.

"Up and at them!" roared the miller's boy, who still hoped it would come to a fight. "Give them a good thrashing!"

"There's the Plumber who carried off the children!" cried a peasant from Aljustrel. "We still have to settle accounts with you, you confounded kidnapper!"

"Police! Police!" cried the editor, wildly waving his arms as he saw the crowd rushing toward him, threatening him with their fists and brandishing sticks.

Poor Bernardo drew his sword and pretended to try to attack the man nearest him with it.

"You'll only hurt yourself with that!" cried the miller's boy, laughing, as he pulled the sword out of the constable's hand and flung it away.

"I can't do anything, Senhor!" cried the agitated policeman to the Prefect. "Someone has taken my sword from me."

The shrieks of laughter that this comic complaint evoked, quelled the anger of the crowd for the moment.

The Prefect cranked up the automobile and muttered hoarsely to the editor: "Start up quickly, man! Don't you see how things are?"

Pale with anger and fear, Senhor do Vale started up the old car. It gave a great bound, then rattled noisily away. The people standing in the path of the snorting vehicle scrambled out of its way just in time. And so the Freemasons retreated amid the laughter of the crowd and the braying of a hundred donkeys.

"I'm really glad someone took my sword from me!" said the constable with a sigh as he went to retrieve it. "If they hadn't, I might have caused a blood bath."

"We must save you, Bernardo!" said the miller's boy, lifting the little man up on his shoulder and carrying him away, kicking and struggling, through the crowd.

When the laughter had died down someone struck up the *Te Deum,* and the solemn hymn of praise resounded all over the Cova.

❧ 11 ❧

HEAVENLY THOUGHTS AND EARTHLY RECKONINGS

That same day Lucia, Francisco and his brother João were herding the sheep in the solitude of Valinhos. Francisco was squatting on a rock near the Cabeço cave, sunk in thought. The air was full of sunlight and very calm. Suddenly the boy raised his eyes in surprise. The sun seemed to darken, although there was not a cloud to be seen, and the blue summer sky assumed a golden tinge.

"Look, Lucia!" he cried excitedly. "Look at the sky—the sun!"

At the same moment there was a flash of lightning on the distant horizon. This was soon followed by a second one.

"That's the sign!" stammered Lucia. Then she turned to her cousin João, who had just brought back a lamb that had strayed away. "João, please run home as quickly as you can and fetch Jacinta! The Blessed Virgin is coming!"

"No, I won't," said the boy obstinately; "I'll stay here! I want to see the miracle, too!"

"Do please go, João!" his cousin begged him. "I have twenty centavos, and I'll give them to you!"

"Twenty centavos? And you'll give them to me?"

"Yes, and you'll get more, too! All you want! But you must fetch Jacinta!"

"Very well! I'll do it for twenty centavos!"

Lucia sighed with relief as she watched her cousin running off. "If only Jacinta arrives in time!" she said.

But it was a good quarter of an hour before the two children arrived back, quite out of breath. Jacinta was not at home, and her brother had had to go to her godmother's house to fetch her.

They had only just arrived back when a white cloud approached from the east and rested above a green oak tree. And again the Celestial Lady appeared to the children. She spoke kindly to them, consoled them for the sufferings they had borne, and told them to come to the Cova again on the thirteenth of September. And she announced once again that a great public miracle would happen in the month of the rosary. Finally a shadow passed over the Blessed Virgin's brow as she said sorrowfully:

"Pray, pray a great deal, and make sacrifices for sinners; for many souls are lost because there is nobody to pray and to make sacrifices for them."

The children remained kneeling there for a long time in a state of rapture, and their eyes followed the cloud in which the Celestial Lady disappeared.

"I didn't see anything!" said João at last, breaking the silence. "I saw nothing but the brightness and the light cloud!"

"Perhaps you were thinking too much about the twenty centavos!" said Lucia, smiling. Then she looked up in surprise at Francisco, who had climbed the oak tree and was cutting off with his penknife the branch on which the Blessed Virgin's foot had rested.

"We shall take it home with us!" he declared. "Why

should we not do the same as the people who have stripped nearly the whole tree in the Cova?"

"Fine!" said Jacinta joyfully. "I'll take it straight home."

"I'll go with you!" said Francisco. "I'm sure you two will be able to manage the sheep alone."

As they were passing in front of the Santos' house, they saw the farmer's wife chatting to a neighbor outside her door.

"Oh, Aunt! We saw the Blessed Virgin at Valinhos!" shouted the little girl, beaming.

"Will you never finish with your lies?" replied the woman crossly. "You're always seeing the Blessed Virgin! I suppose she goes for a walk just wherever you happen to be!"

"Yes, we *have* seen her!" Francisco assured her. "Look at these branches! One of her feet rested on this one, and the other on that one!"

"Give them to me and let me see them!"

"But you must give one of them back to us!" demanded Jacinta.

Meantime Maria-Rosa was examining the two branches of oak. Suddenly she looked up with an astonished expression. "But what kind of a perfume have they? I've never in my life smelled such a perfume; it's like some very costly soap, or incense, or roses! No, it's much more wonderful! Do smell it, neighbor!"

"Yes, it's true!" stammered the other, astonished. "I don't know what it smells like! There's no such perfume anywhere in the world!"

Maria-Rosa, looking thoughtful, returned one branch to the children and carried the other into the house. "If only someone could tell me what kind of a perfume it is!" she said. She carefully wrapped the branch in a piece of linen and laid it in a trunk. "My God!" she said to herself. "Can the children really have been telling the truth, after all?"

In the evening she told her husband about it and showed him the branch, the perfume of which filled the room.

"We do not know if all the children tell us is true," said Antonio. "But neither do we know if it is false. It's really very strange about the branch. Anyway, I won't allow the children to tease Lucia about the apparitions any more."

"The perfume from the branch is certainly no proof," said Maria-Rosa, still doubting. "True, they say that the devil smells horribly, but why should he not be able to mislead people by producing a nice perfume, too?"

A few days later Maria Carreira and her husband came from Moita, called at the Santos' house and asked to speak to the farmer.

"We know well, Senhor dos Santos, that you and the other farmers have suffered great loss with your fields in the Cova da Iria," she said. "You certainly haven't had a good harvest this year."

"It's not only that!" growled the farmer. "It's not only the crops that the people have trampled down. After stripping the evergreen oak, they have now started on the other trees; and they're even tearing the branches off the olive and fig trees."

"We have come to compensate you for the loss you have suffered, and if you agree to it, to buy your land, too. We want to build a chapel in the Cova da Iria. Count it out, Manuel!"

The husband took a fairly large bag from his shoulder and poured out a number of coins and notes onto the table. It was the money which the pilgrims had left as an offering under the tree of the apparition.

Antonio looked with astonishment at the pile of money. It seemed to him as though a harvest of riches were going to rain down on him after all the annoyance and trouble.

"I really don't know what to say!" he said hesitantly. "I'll have to talk it over with my wife first." He called Maria-Rosa, who stared in bewilderment at the money which was heaped on the kitchen table. But when she learned why it was being offered, she refused resolutely to have anything to do with it.

"No, no!" she cried in alarm. "We won't take a centavo of it! Who knows whether the devil may not be behind it all! This money might bring down God's anger on us!"

"How can you say such an outrageous thing?" asked Maria Carreira indignantly. "Thousands of people envy your happiness in being the mother of such a favored child, and you speak of the devil and of divine retribution!"

"In this matter the parish priest alone is qualified to make a decision—not the people. They don't understand these things and are very easily led astray. As long as the priest believes that the devil may have a hand in it, I won't have anything to do with the money nor with anything concerning the Cova da Iria."

"But after all, we have suffered great loss," Antonio reminded her.

"We won't die of hunger on account of that. Take away your money! I don't want to see it on my table any longer!"

"Well, what have you decided? Are you going to sell or not?" asked Manuel Carreira, perplexed.

The farmer shrugged his shoulders and looked enquiringly at his wife.

"We are not selling it!" replied Maria-Rosa.

"Is that your last word?" asked the treasurer of the Cova.

"Yes, it's my last word!" said the farmer's wife, tightening her lips.

"And the chapel? Will you permit us to build a chapel on your land?"

"As far as I am concerned, you may!" muttered Antonio. "And build it as big as you like!"

"That is for the priest to decide," added his wife. With a sigh Manuel Carreira stuffed the money into the bag again and he and Maria left the house deeply disappointed.

An extraordinary number of people wanted to buy the Santos' land in the Cova da Iria during the following days and weeks. Speculators came from Lisbon in big cars and offered the farmer enormous prices for his land. Antonio would have liked very much to sell it, but his wife would not hear of it.

"What a clever, shrewd woman!" remarked one of the dealers as he left the house. "Imagine being offered so much money and not jumping at it! How intelligent she is! Why, she'll get twice as much for it in a couple of months."

The other farmers who owned a bit of land in the Cova did not hesitate. They willingly sold their trampled-down fields when they were offered three or four times the amount they had expected, and they celebrated the business exuberantly in Guimarães' tavern.

"So you were right after all, old fox!" they said to the wandering musician, who in the meantime had atoned for his insulting words to the Mayor. "You're a confoundedly cunning fellow!"

"And all of you insist, on the other hand, on being stupid fools! In a year from now you'd get ten times the price for your land!"

The farmers looked at each other perplexed, and then they said they were quite pleased with what they had received, and anyway no one could say how the matter might yet end.

"You can still ask that?" said Luis with a grin. "When the city folk put so much money down on the table, you may be sure they know what they're doing. Just wait and see! In a few years more there will be the most beautiful hotels and the finest shops in Fatima."

"Hotels in Fatima indeed!" exclaimed the tavern keeper, shaking his head. "You don't even believe that yourself!"

"If I were as rich as you are, I'd buy a piece of land myself near the Cova!" said the artful fellow. "Then you could build a hotel on it. The banks in Lisbon would advance you enough money, and you would soon be cashing in bagfuls of escudos. You will see, Fatima will become the Lourdes of Portugal! You may be sure of that!"

"The deuce take it! I must think the matter over!" said Guimarães thoughtfully.

But one of the farmers said, "It won't ever be like that. Fatima will never be a big place of pilgrimage!"

"But why not?" asked others. "Do you not believe in the apparitions?"

"Yes, I do believe in them! But all the same, Fatima won't become a great place of pilgrimage. There are no springs in the whole Serra, and already the pilgrims have drunk almost all the cisterns dry."

The men fell silent, disconcerted, and the tavern keeper said with an air of satisfaction: "It's a good thing that soon there will not be a drop of water left in Fatima. The people will drink all the more wine!" He was thinking with pleasure of the good business he had done on the 13th of August. Truly, heavenly thoughts and earthly calculations ran side by side in those days.

❧12❧

A SIGN IN THE SKY

It was hard to get a moment's quiet in Aljustrel. Every day people came wanting to see the children, and it was almost impossible for their parents to get through the most necessary work. The children themselves found the everlasting questions worry enough, especially since many of the visitors refused to be convinced of the truth.

"Why do you ask, if you don't want to believe?" Lucia would often say to them with a sigh. But Jacinta thought that this constant interrogation was at least a good opportunity of offering a sacrifice to God. But it hurt the children—especially when priests doubted their words.

One day Dom Manuel Carreira Poças, the parish priest of Pôrto de Mos, arrived at the Marto's house. He was the same priest who had come to Fatima on the 13th of August with the Prefect.

"This matter leaves me no peace! I must question the children once more!" he explained.

"Very well, then, question them, Father," replied Ti Manuel with a sigh. But when they fetched Lucia from the fields, the priest showered reproaches on her.

"Listen, child!" he said excitedly. "Admit now that you did not see anything, that everything you said was lies, or a mistake, or deceit. If you don't do that, I'll tell everyone and spread it about. You'll see, you will be burned as a witch, and none of your homes will be spared either."

This was too much for Farmer Marto. "For all I care you may do as you like, Father!" he said angrily. "Telephone it around everywhere, and lose no time about it!"

"Yes, certainly, that must be done!"

"Why then are you waiting all this time for admissions? Leave the children in peace! No one is preventing you from doing whatever you think you should do!"

"Well, where are your children?" asked the priest irritably. "I want to speak to them, too."

"They cannot be very far away!" answered the farmer brusquely. "You can look for them yourself! We have something better to do than continually running out after them."

Dom Manuel found Jacinta in the neighborhood. She was combing the hair of another little girl.

"Listen, Jacinta!" he said to her. "I've just come from your cousin Lucia. She has admitted that it is all nothing but lies!"

"She didn't say that, Father!" replied Jacinta promptly.

"Oh, yes, she admitted it."

"No, she didn't do that!" repeated Jacinta calmly, continuing to comb the hair of the child.

"But I tell you that she did confess it!" insisted the priest.

"It's not true!" said the child, smiling. "Now, don't move your head, Christina!"

Ti Manuel, who had followed the priest, watched the latter's disappointed face with a certain mischievous pleasure. At last, disconcerted, the priest pulled out his purse, searched for a coin, and offered it to Jacinta. But the child, hardly glancing at it, started to plait the other little girl's hair.

"You can put away your money!" said the farmer. "We don't want any of that sort of thing!"

"I only meant well!" stammered the priest, embarrassed. "You know, it's a matter of the truth, and the honor of the Church."

"I willingly excuse you on that account," said Manuel. "But tell me, Father, have you yourself been so very careful about telling the truth just now?"

The parish priest of Pŏrto de Mos set off for home feeling rather dispirited. Lucia's firmness and little Jacinta's calm certainty had shaken his doubts more than he cared to admit.

A few days later another priest knocked at the door of the Dos Santos' home. Lucia sighed sadly when she was called.

"Oh, the questioning starting again!" she said. But when she entered the room and saw who her visitor was, her face lit up with joy.

"Father Cruz! Oh, how wonderful that you have come!" she cried joyfully. It was the priest who, four years previously, had obtained permission from the parish priest of Fatima for her to make her First Holy Communion and who was revered as a saint throughout the country. Even at that time, when people used to throw stones at priests in the cities, nobody dared to insult this great and charitable priest.

"I wanted so much to see you once more, child!" said the priest cordially. "The people are talking a lot now about Fatima and its miraculous apparitions. So old Father Cruz got up on his donkey and rode along here. It was a very long journey, very long indeed, both for the donkey and its rider."

"Oh, I'll gladly tell you everything!" cried Lucia, looking radiant. "But first I'll run and get Francisco and Jacinta. They will be so glad, too; I've told them so much about you."

Shortly afterward the four of them set off for the Cova da Iria. The little donkey on which Dom Francisco da Cruz rode was so small that the priest's feet were almost touching the ground, so it was quite easy to talk to him as they went along.

"You poor children!" said the priest. "How you have been tormented with questions! Well, I don't want to hear anything more from you than what you want to tell me yourselves."

This time the children told everything willingly and with great enthusiasm. The priest listened quietly and attentively without interrupting them.

"I know that you're not telling me lies!" he said at last. "God has given me in my old age something of the gift of being able to read hearts. I know that there is neither wickedness nor deceit in yours. How happy you must be, and how much you must love the Blessed Virgin and Our Lord!"

"Oh, yes, Father! With all our hearts!" Jacinta assured him.

"I really believe that Almighty God listens to your prayers very specially," continued the priest. "And in these times, particularly, the world has great need of the pious prayers of children. The Church in our country has a heavy cross to bear at the present time. And so has the Holy Father in Rome. My God, what troubles he has and how great is his responsibility! How immense is his sorrow for his children who are slaughtering each other with the deadly weapons of war instead of letting their wounds heal, and loving each other! So offer your sufferings, not only for sinners but also for the Pope."

"If only I could see the Pope one day!" said Jacinta with a sigh. "So many people come here, but the Holy Father does not come. How I would love to show him the Cova da Iria!"

"He would surely see the Blessed Virgin himself then!" said Francisco with conviction. "But why doesn't he come?"

"Ah, the poor Holy Father lives like a prisoner in St. Peter's in Rome!" said the priest with a sad smile. "He cannot get up on a donkey and ride along here as easily as old Father Cruz can. Pray a great deal for the Pope!"

At last they reached the Cova. The priest gazed for a long time at the tree over which the Blessed Virgin had appeared. Then he beckoned the children to him and said with great emotion, "When you see the Mother of God again, pray for this old man, too!" Then he blessed the three children and rode away.

That was the nicest visit the children had received up till then, and they often thought of Father Cruz afterward. His words and exhortations had made a deep impression on their hearts.

The clergy were still much divided in their opinions. Some believed, others doubted, and there were many who said it was all a fraud or a machination of the devil. The Archbishop of Lisbon had ordered the priests to be very reserved until the matter had been officially clarified, and had forbidden them to take part in any religious demonstrations in the Cova da Iria or support them in any way. Therefore, the parish priest of Fatima definitely refused to consent to a chapel being built. Of course, the ecclesiastical authorities had instructed some learned theologians to investigate the matter, and to be present as observers at the events which were expected to take place in the Cova. There were also some priests who felt that it was permissible for them to observe events discreetly from a distance.

It was thus that on Thursday the 13th of September, Dom Joaquim Ferreira das Neves, the parish priest of Santa Catarina, set out for Fatima. He was the priest who from the pulpit had forbidden his parishioners to visit the Cova da Iria. The nearer he approached to the village the more difficult it was for him to make his way through with his little horse trap, for all the roads were crowded with pilgrims bound for the same goal. They came from great distances on donkeys, on bicycles and in automobiles, but most of them were walking, many of them barefooted. There were people of every age and state—nobility in magnificent carriages, merchants, officials, city folk, peasants, devout pilgrims, inquisitive people and scoffers, and a whole army of traders and beggars hoping to do good business. Half the country seemed to be on its way to Fatima.

Tired and perspiring, the parish priest arrived at last at the village of the apparitions, and dismounted at the rectory. There he found many other priests, some of whom had come from a long way off. Among them were that great scholar, Dr. Formigão, a Canon, and Professor at the Diocesan Seminary in Santarém; Dom João Quaresma, a worthy Monsignor of Leiria, and many others. And of course the parish priest of Pôrto de Mos, one of the most determined opponents of belief in the apparitions, was there, too. Dom Joaquim found his colleagues in the midst of an excited discussion.

"I came here quite unprejudiced," Dr. Formigão was in the act of explaining, "but I must say I am deeply impressed by what I have seen since I have been here."

"It is just the same with me," said the Monsignor. "I was in the Cova, where thousands have spent the whole night. Of course I saw all the business activity of the traders and the importunity of the beggars, and heard the mocking remarks of the incredulous. But I also noticed the fervor with which most of the people were saying the rosary and the patience with which they were enduring the scorching heat. All that impressed me greatly, I willingly admit."

"What you say to me is nothing new, Monsignor," said the parish priest of Fatima anxiously. "What troubles me most is the thought that the devil may be exploiting the religious fervor of the faithful to deceive them."

"A game of the devil. Yes, that's what it is and nothing else," agreed Dom Joaquim.

"I still think it's just a common fraud!" declared Dom Manuel, the parish priest of Pôrto de Mos, obstinately.

"No, it is not a fraud!" said Dom Marcus, shaking his head wearily. "After all, you questioned the children yourself several times. Did you get the impression that they were telling lies?"

"If this concerned some ordinary everyday matter, I would feel compelled to believe," admitted Dom Manuel, embarrassed.

"If the children seem to be trustworthy, why then should one not believe them?" asked the Monsignor from Leiria.

"I believe, gentlemen, that all our surmising is a little premature," said Dr. Formigão. "It's getting on toward midday now, and I suggest that we go to the Cova da Iria. Afterward we shall know better where we are."

"Still, it's nothing but the work of the devil!" muttered the parish priest of Santa Catarina.

It was almost impossible to force one's way along in the Cova da Iria. Twenty to thirty thousand people were crowded into the broad valley. Traders were shouting their wares; beggars were showing their infirmities and asking alms. The tavern keeper Guimarães was doing good business, although he was now no longer the only one offering wine and other drinks for sale. And Luis, the village piper, was there too with his medals and rosary beads, calling out, "Guaranteed to have touched the holy tree of the miracle."

"All that is more than repugnant!" asserted Dom Joaquim, and the parish priest of Pôrto de Mos nodded agreement. The farther they proceeded, the more dense the crowd became, but the fervor with which the believers prayed and waited for the apparition, also became more evident and moving.

At last a murmur, followed by excited shouts, ran through the crowd. The people had caught sight of the three children and the multitude pressed around them from every side. People even called down from the trees that they had climbed:

"For the love of God pray for my paralyzed son!"

"Ask the Blessed Virgin to make my blind child see!"

"Ask that my husband may come home safe from the war!"

"For love of the Holy Madonna, pray for a poor sinner who is very dear to me!"

Wives and mothers threw themselves on their knees before the children, begging them with tears and sobs to intercede for their men. All the sorrow of the world seemed to assail the children. The gray flood of misery and distress overwhelmed their young hearts. Trembling with emotion, the children promised to remember each intention, and begged the crowd to let them pass through. Jacinta clung timidly to her father, who would not move a step from her side. In this way they reached the holy spot at last.

"Did you see that, brother?" cried Dom Joaquim, the parish priest of Santa Catarina, indignantly. "A woman has knelt down in front of Lucia and asked for her blessing, as if she were an anointed priest and not a little ten-year-old girl."

"It's simply revolting!" cried Dom Manuel.

Dr. Formigão, the delegate of the ecclesiastical authorities in Lisbon, succeeded in finding a place from which he was able to observe the children. The worthy priest felt very sorry for the little ones who were being importuned and pushed about from every side.

"Well, they certainly don't look like frauds," he whispered to the Monsignor at his side. Monsignor Quaresma was far too moved to be able to answer him.

When they arrived at the little evergreen oak, Lucia asked the crowd to say the rosary with them, and she herself began by reciting the Apostles' Creed in a loud voice.

"The little trickster does it quite cleverly!" hissed Dom Manuel. The Hail Mary was taken up again and again by ten thousand voices.

At midday exactly, the sun lost its brilliance and a

golden-yellow glow covered the sky just as during the previous apparitions. Suddenly Lucia interrupted her prayers, and pointing excitedly toward the east, cried:

"There she comes! Oh, look! Look!"

The prayers came to an end. The roar died away with a sound like the last wash of an ebbing wave. Then a cry rose up over the Cova. Ten thousand hands stretched out in the direction toward which Lucia was pointing and the crowd cried:

"Look! Look! Oh, my God! How beautiful it is! How beautiful!"

A globe of light as if illuminated by a thousand stars was advancing from the east. It glided along slowly and majestically, coming nearer and nearer, and finally disappearing from view.

"I still see it!" cried a girl. "It's moving off there over the hills!"

"Oh, my God!" murmured Monsignor Quaresma, and made the sign of the cross.

A strange light remained above the holy tree which the celestial globe had touched. Dr. Formigão saw the expression of holy expectation on the children's faces change and give place to a beatific, other-worldly gaze of profound contemplation. The noise of the crowd died down, and everyone stared, motionless, in the direction of the children, trying to catch Lucia's voice. They heard her begging that the sick might be healed and that all the petitions which had been entrusted to her might be heard. Then the little girl seemed to stop and listen.

Lucia told the invisible being of the people's wish to build a chapel at the Cova. Then they heard the child crying out in a sorrowful voice, "Many people scold me and say I'm a liar. They say I should be hanged or burned. Do please work a miracle, dear Lady, and make them believe!"

Again something very puzzling happened.

"Look! Look!" shouted thousands of people as they pointed to the evergreen oak.

A silvery cloud floated down from the sky to the tree of the apparitions, remained over it for a moment, then disappeared as if blown away by the wind. This happened twice.

"It is as though the angels were swinging a censer in front of the Queen of Heaven!" the Professor whispered to his neighbor, whose eyes were filled with tears of emotion.

Again there was a cry of astonishment. While the glow of light still shone over the oak tree, something else, something quite strange and incomprehensible, happened. A rain of white, gleaming flakes came down from the cloudless sky. "It's snowing, it's snowing in the middle of summer!" people cried.

"No, it's blossoms that are falling—pure white roses!" cried others. Those who had room enough opened their parasols and held them upside down to catch some of the snowlike shower of flowers. But the miraculous rain did not reach the ground; at some distance up, the gleaming flakes vanished.

"Look! Look!" cried Dom Joaquim, gripping his neighbor excitedly by the arm. "My God, no! That is not from the devil! I believe, Dom Manuel, I believe!"

The parish priest of Pôrto de Mos had turned white as a sheet. "No, no. It's delusion and deceit! It's a phantasm which I cannot explain! Delusion and deceit! Delusion and deceit!" he repeated trembling with agitation.

Dom Joaquim no longer heard him. He forced his way

through the crowd, fell on his knees as if impelled by an invisible force, and prayed in a loud voice.

Meanwhile, the golden globe again approached the tree of the apparition, hovered over it for a moment, and then floated away toward the east.

"She's leaving us! The Blessed Virgin is leaving us!" the bystanders heard Lucia crying out. "She's no longer to be seen!"

The people crowded around the children to learn what the Celestial Being had said to them. The two girls repeated again and again what they had heard. The Blessed Virgin had promised to cure some of the sick people before the year would end. She approved of the plan to build a chapel, and she promised once more that a great miracle would happen in October. In the end some sturdy men had to carry the children out of the crowd.

"And now, what have you got to say?" the Monsignor asked the Professor from Santarém very excitedly.

"What can I say?" replied Dr. Formigão. "What are words? What indeed are words?" Then remembering the task entrusted to him, the delegate of the ecclesiastical authorities walked about from one group to another in order to find out what the people had seen. True, there were some who said they had seen nothing at all, but this testimony was far outweighed by that of the thousands who had seen the miraculous signs.

Once more the priests met in the rectory. The parish priest of Fatima, who had chosen to remain away from the Cova da Iria, was utterly dumfounded on hearing his colleagues' reports.

"But may it not be a machination of the devil?" he finally asked uncertainly.

"No, brother, definitely not!" replied the parish priest of Santa Catarina passionately. "You know that I have always spoken against the apparitions, both among my colleagues and also from the pulpit. But now I know that this comes, not from the devil, but from God."

The Monsignor from Leiria agreed entirely and just as fervently.

"And what do you think, Professor?"

"I admit that I have been deeply impressed," said Dr. Formigão. "Yet there are people who did not see the marvelous signs. I must make certain about it. So first of all I shall stay at Fatima, and above all question the children thoroughly. The Patriarchate in Lisbon has ordered me to do this. I regret therefore that as a delegate from the archbishopric I still have to doubt, while as a man and a priest I should like to say a thousand times: 'I believe!'"

"My word, it seems to me that I am the only one of you who has kept his senses!" said Dom Manuel passionately. "Once again I solemnly declare: I do not believe!" Saying this, he turned to the door and went away exasperated.

When Dom Marcus was alone once more, he sat with his head in his hands and groaned. "May God release me from my doubts!" he murmured. "The weight of responsibility is crushing me!"

❧ 13 ❧

THE ANXIOUS WAIT

On Wednesday, the 27th of September, Professor Formigão called at the Santos' home.

"I'm very sorry if I am disturbing you, my good woman," he said politely to Maria-Rosa, who stood up from her spinning wheel, visibly annoyed by the constant visits.

"You must understand, Father," she said with a sigh, "that it's becoming almost impossible to get through the most necessary work." When the priest told her, however, that he came by order of the diocesan authorities, she changed her attitude completely. "Oh, in that case you have the right to question the children!" she said.

She hurriedly wiped a chair with her apron and invited the priest to sit down in the little room. "I'll send for Lucia at once!" she said. "She's helping to gather the grapes in our little vineyard, but she'll be here soon."

"And the two other children?"

"I think Jacinta is playing in the street. Francisco is minding the sheep in Valinhos with his brother João and our Carolina. I'll get someone to call them, too!"

It was not long before Jacinta arrived. She looked timidly at the strange priest, who was agreeably pleased at the sight of the little girl. With her sunburned face and her dress almost touching her feet, she stood before him a picture of childish freshness and health.

Now the torture is starting again! thought Jacinta. Another priest who will ask a hundred questions and in the end won't believe a word! Her fear did not diminish in the least when she saw the strange priest lay some sheets of paper in front of him on the shaky table and take a fountain pen out of his pocket.

"You need not be afraid, my child," said the Professor with a kind smile. "I suppose you know that the Archbishop of Lisbon has been expelled from the country by the enemies of the Church, but his representative has sent me here. He wants to know exactly what has taken place in the Cova da Iria. Will you answer my questions?"

The little girl nodded, still very frightened.

"You must tell the gentleman what you know!" Maria-Rosa warned her, then returned to her spinning wheel.

But the little girl was so shy that she was hardly able to utter an intelligible word. She was greatly relieved when Francisco came in, wearing his long peaked cap. Jacinta made secret signs to him to take off his cap. The boy took no notice but sat down and looked expectantly at the priest.

"You're not afraid of me, are you?" asked the Professor, smiling. "After all, you're already a little man and wear long trousers."

"I'm not afraid!" Francisco assured him confidently. "Ask me whatever you like! We're used to it."

"Good. Then we two shall begin. Your little sister can go outside and play for the present."

The little girl disappeared out of the door like the wind, and this very important questioning of the boy began in the low, narrow little room of the peasant's house. Francisco replied to all the questions openly and sincerely, and without having to think for long. He looked at the priest frankly and calmly with his big dark eyes.

"What did you see in the Cova da Iria in the last few months?"

"I saw the Blessed Virgin."

"Where did she appear?"

"Above the little evergreen oak."

"Does she appear suddenly, or do you see her coming along from one side?"

"She comes from the side where the sun rises and then she remains over the oak."

"Does she come slowly or quickly?"

"She always comes quickly."

"Do you understand what she says to Lucia?"

"I don't hear any of it."

"Have you spoken to the Lady?"

"No, I haven't asked her anything. She only speaks to Lucia."

"Whom does she look at—all three of you, or only Lucia?"

"All three of us, but Lucia most."

"Has she wept or smiled sometimes?"

"She is always serious."

"How is she dressed?"

"She has a long dress, and over it a cloak which covers her head and reaches down to the hem of her dress."

"What color are the dress and the cloak?"

"They are white. The hem of the dress is edged with gold."

"How does the Lady stand?"

"As if she were praying. She has her hands clasped in front of her breast."

"Does she hold anything in her hand?"

"She has a rosary over her right hand and it hangs down over her dress."

"Does she wear earrings?"

"One cannot see if she does, because her ears are covered by the cloak."

"What color are the beads of the rosary?"

"They are also white."

"Is the Lady beautiful?"

"Oh, indeed she is!"

"Is she more beautiful than that girl who is walking across the street outside? Come to the window and look at her!"

"Much more beautiful!" replied Francisco in a disdainful tone. "She is a thousand times more beautiful than anyone I have ever seen before."

The Professor wrote down all the replies.

"Well, you have answered me very clearly and candidly, as becomes a man!" he said at last. "Now go and bring in your sister!"

"She's very bashful, Father!" said the boy, laughing.

"Then tell her that she need not be afraid."

"Yes, I'll do that." Francisco kissed the priest's hand and went to fetch his sister. "You needn't be frightened, he won't bite," he whispered into Jacinta's ear.

"Is that true?" asked the little girl timidly.

"Yes, quite true!"

So Jacinta gathered her courage and answered simply and honestly.

The priest asked her the same questions as he had asked

Francisco, and the child gave the same answers. She described the apparition of the Celestial Lady in exactly the same way. She only hesitated when asked if the Blessed Virgin carried the rosary in her left hand or in her right. The poor little girl was not sure which was the right and which was the left. But when the priest handed her his rosary and asked her to hold it up as the Mother of God had held hers, she was able to do so accurately.

Finally, Lucia arrived. Jacinta ran up to her joyfully, her little face beaming with happiness. The ten-year-old girl answered the questions with perfect assurance and described the appearance and bearing of the Lady in exactly the same way as the others, only adding that the Blessed Virgin's dress had a golden cord around it, which was fastened by a knot and had a tassel. She reported all that the Blessed Virgin had said with the exception of the secret message. She kept silent only with regard to this.

When the questioning was over Dr. Formigão blessed the children and returned to the rectory, where he was residing during his stay in Fatima.

"What was your impression, Professor?" asked Dom Marcus anxiously.

"The children seem to be definitely trustworthy," replied Formigão. "They answered me freely without a trace of embarrassment. All their statements agree completely, and I could not see the slightest sign of any peculiarity which would indicate psychic disturbance. The three are typical children of our mountains, obviously healthy in mind and body. Certainly none of them shows any indication of being highly strung or subject to hysterical hallucinations."

"I share your conviction in that," said the parish priest thoughtfully. "However, all that does not prove to me that they are not the unfortunate victims of some diabolical game."

"My dear colleague!" said Dr. Formigão with a smile. "Why precisely do you persist in thinking that the devil has something to do with it? Is it not much more credible that God should give a sign to the world in the Cova da Iria? I have seen the stream of pilgrims and witnessed the fervor with which they prayed. Believe me, our unhappy Portugal, which is threatened with the loss of its religion and its traditions under the godless government, is turning back to God, owing to the apparitions in Fatima. Could that really be the work of the devil?"

"Your interpretation seems to me to be justified, but think of the harm the Church will suffer if the happenings in the Cova da Iria prove to be error and delusion! I almost seem to hear the hellish laughter of our enemies. And what if the prophesied miracle on the 13th of October does not happen?"

"I am convinced that it will happen!" replied the Professor. "No, no, my dear friend, I am not credulous! And as delegate of the Diocesan Ordinary, it is my duty to play the devil's advocate. I cannot accept mere grounds for probability; I must have irrefutable certainty. That is why I am following up every possible trail, leaving scope for every possible objection, and doubting on principle wherever I can possibly doubt. I have done everything to obtain a reliable picture of the matter. I have questioned the children separately, and shall question them again and again. I have spoken to the parents, to acquaintances and relatives, to friends and to persons opposed to belief in the apparitions. In fact it is to these opponents that I have listened with special attention. True, I have not finished my enquiries yet, and it will probably be a long time before the Church, which is and must always be extremely cautious in such matters, makes a pronouncement. But if you ask my personal impression, I must admit that I am already practically convinced that the Mother of God did appear to the children and speak to them. Anyhow, we shall see what happens on the 13th of October."

"I'm thinking of that day with horror!" said Dom Marcus sighing.

There were others who felt as troubled as did the parish priest. Everywhere people were saying frightening things to the children and to their parents.

"My God, if there is no miracle you'll be torn to pieces!" they called to the children on the streets. "You'll be burned alive, you may be sure of it!"

"Don't go to the Cova on the thirteenth!" other well-meaning people said to them. "Hide yourselves! Go as far away as you can! If the promised miracle does not take place, you shan't get home alive!"

But the three children were not intimidated.

"The Blessed Virgin has promised the miracle, so it will happen!" they replied with complete confidence.

A few days before the decisive date, they were minding their sheep at Valinhos. The land was full of light and sunshine as far as the eyes could see, right over to the distant hills on which the windmills were turning. Francisco was sitting on a stone near the grotto of Cabeço, playing a merry tune on his sugar-cane flute, while the girls were plaiting a wreath of flowers and humming the tune.

"My word! How happy and peaceful you all are!" they suddenly heard a familiar voice saying. None of them had heard Luis, the village piper, coming. He now sat down beside Francisco with a merry greeting. "You are singing and playing just as if you did not know that you would be boiled and roasted next Saturday."

"You're joking again, Luis!" said the boy, laughing and taking up his flute to resume playing.

"Who would boil and roast us?" asked Jacinta. "Why, even the Prefect in Ourém didn't do that!"

"Yes, but it's a serious matter this time!" said the piper with a sigh. And the children noticed that he really looked troubled. "Listen! You know I'm no coward. I was in the same regiment with your father. In Africa I strangled lions and tigers with my bare hands, and I've walked over a dozen crocodiles as I would over a wooden bridge. You can ask your father if I'm telling the truth."

"We did ask him," said the boy gleefully, "and he said you are a boaster and that not a tenth of what you say is true."

"How could you tell such lies!" said Lucia reproachfully. "You know that to tell lies is a sin that offends God."

"Well, perhaps I did make a mistake about a few details!" replied Luis, embarrassed. "After all, it's a long time now since I hunted lions, and I only told you the story to show you that I am not a man to be afraid. But if I were in your shoes, ten horses wouldn't drag me to the Cova da Iria next Saturday."

"But why not?" asked Jacinta surprised.

"Don't you understand what I'm driving at yet?" said Luis, now really worried. "How many people do you think will come to the Cova da Iria on the 13th of October? Why, thousands and tens of thousands! Most of them will come from far off and will have had a whole day's walk to get to Fatima. And what if no miracle happens, children? Just imagine how it will be! They'll think you have been fooling them, and they'll beat you to death in their disappointment. I'm not joking or humbugging this time, but speaking the bitter truth."

The girls were quite unaffected by what Luis said and continued to plait their wreath of blossoms to decorate the evergreen oak in the Cova da Iria. Francisco began to play a merry tune on his flute and was not in the least disturbed either by the terrible threats.

"Look at that mill over there!" said Luis, pointing to a nearby hill. "There are two great stones in there which grind the corn as fine as dust. Now, depend on it, the people will put you three into a bag and throw you into the cage of the mill. And how much do you think will be left of you then?"

"That's funny!" laughed the boy. "Always a new story! First we're to be beaten to death, then we're to be hanged, then torn in pieces, then boiled and roasted, and now we're to be stuck into the mill, too. I'd just love to know how they'll manage to do it all."

"Children, I do beg of you by all that's dear to me to stop the joking! You know I wish you well and I am not trying to frighten you just for fun. The matter is really serious. You're playing with your lives if you go to the Cova on the thirteenth, for if the miracle does not happen . . ."

"But it will happen!" said Lucia quietly. "The Blessed Virgin promised that a miracle would happen, so it will happen. That's quite simple, isn't it? What should we be afraid of?"

"It's no good talking to you!" grumbled the piper. "If I had known that, I'd have spared myself the long walk here. So you're really going to the Cova on Saturday, are you?"

"Yes, of course!" replied Jacinta eagerly.

"Very well, then I shall do my best to protect you. Perhaps it won't be much good, but anyway I'll try to hunt up a few old army comrades to lend me a hand. I'll lose the best chance of business I've ever had in my life, for I won't sell a single set of rosary beads but stay beside you three all the time."

A melancholy smile passed over the sun-tanned face of the old wandering player. "After all, we've all been in the same prison and former jailbirds always hang together," he continued. "That's the way all over the world! And now, good-by and God be with you!" With a sigh he stood up and shook hands with each child. "Perhaps after all you'll get out of the hurly-burly alive. If not, old Luis will be the first to be torn to pieces."

The children looked after the piper for a long time as he walked sadly away over the stony path.

"Luis is the best fellow in the world!" said Francisco. "If only he were not so frightened!"

In Aljustrel too the people became more and more anxious as the day of the miracle approached. Farmer Santos grumbled continually in his effort to hide his worry; the two mothers prayed a great deal; and Ti Manuel forgot his jokes.

Neighbors came and advised the parents not to go to the valley themselves. "Perhaps people will be afraid to do any harm to the innocent children, but they'll certainly kill you if there's no miracle," they said.

"I'd be a nice father indeed if I left my children in the lurch in face of such danger!" said Manuel Pedro, resolutely shaking his head. "Of course we'll go with the children!"

Even Antonio dos Santos said he would remain by Lucia whatever happened.

On Friday Maria-Rosa took her daughter aside and said to her, "We shall go to Confession today!"

"But why, Mother?" the girl asked surprised.

"We don't know how things will turn out tomorrow. If the Blessed Virgin does not work the miracle as promised, the people will kill us. So it's best for us to be ready to die!"

"Oh, then you also believe that it really was the Blessed Virgin whom we have seen!" said the girl beaming with joy. For that was all she had taken in of her mother's words.

"I said we should go to Confession!" the mother repeated.

"Yes, of course, we'll go to Confession if you wish it!" answered the girl. "But I am not doing so because I am afraid we will die. The Blessed Virgin promised the miracle, so it will happen."

"That's all you ever say!" said her mother wearily.

As though the terrible threats were not enough, somebody reported in great agitation that he had definite information the Freemasons were plotting an attack. They were going to lay a mine near the evergreen oak that would explode at the moment of the apparition and blow the children to pieces.

"Rubbish!" muttered Ti Manuel.

But Jacinta cried, "That would be a great stroke of luck for us. Then the Blessed Virgin would take us straight to heaven with her!"

It began to rain toward midday, but, in spite of the bad weather, pilgrims were streaming into Fatima from every direction. Many of these people first visited the church and remained there praying until dark. Pedro, the old sacristan, waited impatiently to lock up the church, loudly rattling his bunch of keys as a hint.

Gradually the church emptied until only one person remained kneeling in front of the statue of Our Lady of Mount Carmel. The sacristan frowned angrily when he saw she was Luisa, the sinner of Fatima.

"I have to lock the church!" he whispered to her.

"Yes, lock it up!" said the girl, nodding.

"Then may I ask you to finish your devotions for today!" said the old man.

"Please let me stay here!" pleaded the outcast. "I have so much to say to the Blessed Virgin!"

"But surely you don't want to spend the whole night here?"

"Yes, I do. Please let me stay!"

"That's quite out of the question; I'll have to ask the parish priest first."

Luisa did not answer. The old man shuffled along to the rectory and reported the strange matter.

"Let her remain in the church in the name of God!" replied the priest. "Perhaps it is a good thing for someone to pray all the night through."

"But—a woman like that?" asked the sacristan hesitantly.

The priest looked at him sharply. "You would do well to read the Gospel story of the Publican and the Pharisee," he said.

The sacristan shuffled back to the church, muttering to himself, and locked the door.

Luisa had been driven to the church by an indefinable fear. Now she was kneeling before the picture of Our Lady of Joys. She prayed silently for a long time. She, the sinner condemned by everyone, had a presentiment of the mystery of Fatima before anyone else had. The guilt of the world, which had been crying to God since the beginning of time, had pushed open the gates of heaven. Now God gave His answer. The answer did not come in the form of thunder, however, but as a message of grace. God's hour was at hand, and He spoke through the mouth of His Mother, not to judge the world but to save it from judgment.

Luisa thought of her own sins, and she felt convinced that the Blessed Virgin had appeared to save her when she called on the children to make reparation. Like everyone else in the village, she knew the danger the three little seers were in, and her heart nearly stopped beating at the thought that perhaps God would demand sacrifice of the innocent for the guilty. Oppressed with these thoughts she bowed her head down to the cold flagstones and offered her own life to God as a sacrifice.

It rained the whole night through; nevertheless the endless processions along the muddy roads to Fatima continued. There were no accommodations available in the few poor cottages, so the immense crowds, freezing with cold and wet through, camped about the Cova da Iria. People tried to light fires but the rain quenched them again, yet no one thought of going away. The hours dragged on endlessly; there could be no thought of sleep. The pilgrims recited the rosary aloud and sang hymns in honor of the Blessed Virgin. It was the great night vigil of Fatima.

The dawn came gray and late. It was still pouring rain and more and more pilgrims were arriving in the village. There were fisherfolk from Vieira, who had left their little cottages by the sea; woodcutters from the mountains; cowherds from Ribatejo, wearing knee breeches, white stockings, boleros and colored caps; students from Coimbra in their long, fringed university cloaks; weavers from Porto; farmers and shepherds from the Alentejo in leather breeches, sheepskin coats and wolf-fur collars; fishwives from Nazaré in their national dress; scholars; newspaper reporters; artisans; townsfolk and beggars; people of all stations and callings. The whole country was on pilgrimage to the scene of the apparitions in order to see the miracle. Cyclists got stuck in the mud. Horse carts and automobiles pushed on slowly. Buses had to crawl along because it was not possible to make their way through. A great human avalanche was rolling down the mountain paths—men and women in long cloaks, heavy with rain, carrying a basket or a bag of food on their heads, most of them barefooted, some of them leaning heavily on long sticks, others with open umbrellas.

But of what use were umbrellas when the wind was mercilessly blowing the cold rain against their faces? Those who were not driving in a covered vehicle got wet to the skin. At every step the mud splashed up to the pilgrims' knees. The cars splashed the pedestrians with water from the puddles, yet seldom was a word of complaint heard. The pilgrims continued on their way undeterred, all their thoughts bent toward the longed-for goal. The streets of Fatima became filled with the tumult of automobiles, horse carts, oxcarts, donkeys, bicycles and pedestrians. Yet again and again the traffic blocks loosened up because everyone was so intent on making room for his neighbor as far as possible.

But the rain kept on and on. Water was dripping from dresses and coats, from broad-brimmed sombreros, from umbrellas, and from the people's faces. The only people who blessed the rain were the farmers of Fatima. They were thinking of the 13th of October with intense anxiety because they feared that the pilgrims would use up the last drop of water they had. The rain was at least filling up the empty cisterns.

Actually, the people feared that in such weather there would not be the signs from heaven which accompanied the earlier apparitions.

"You will see!" they whispered one to another. "There will be no miracle today! But what will happen to the children in that case?"

⚜ 14 ⚜

IN THE COVA DA IRIA

Shortly before midday, Dr. Formigão left the rectory of Fatima. On the road which led from Vila Nova de Ourém to Batalha a car drew up beside him.

"Won't you get in, Professor?" the driver, an intelligent-looking young man, called to him. "You will get to the place of the apparitions more easily in my car. You know me, don't you? Or have you forgotten your former pupil from the Santarém Seminary?"

"Thank you, Senhor de Almeida!" replied the Professor, getting in. "You are very kind. No, I have not forgotten you; I remember you every morning in my Mass."

"Do you believe that can be of any help to an inveterate Freemason?" asked the young man sarcastically. "And by the way, did you read my last article in the *Século* about the apparitions?"

"I know you're now chief editor of that great Lisbon newspaper. Yes, I have read your article. Actually, it was much more objective than the articles the *Século* has been publishing up to now, though you were not quite able to suppress a few cynical remarks. The hymns of hate which you wrote for the *Laterna* were far worse."

"We are definitely in two different camps!" said the editor with a shrug. "With us it's like poor Lazarus and the rich reveler. There is an insurmountable gulf between us —unfortunately! I liked you very much when I was with you in Santarém, and I still esteem you today, although our ways have parted so completely. But what do you actually think about the apparitions? I cannot really imagine such a learned and highly intelligent man as you believing in them."

"Perhaps you will believe in them too by the time you return to Lisbon!"

"In that case very strange things will have to happen in the Cova da Iria!" said the Freemason, laughing. "But I'm quite willing to be surprised."

The car could only crawl along very slowly on account of the crowds. Again and again Almeida had to stop, and he was forced to move with the crowd until they arrived at the Cova. He drew up at the edge of the valley, but, because of the continuous downpour, he did not get out. Dr. Formigão, however, got out, thanked him for the lift and proceeded to push his way through the throng.

"Do stay here!" the editor urged him. "You won't be able to get through!" But the Professor would not remain.

As he could not open his umbrella on account of the crush, he was soaked to the skin in a few moments. It was impossible to avoid the numerous puddles, and soon the water soaked through his far from watertight shoes. Yet he tried to get nearer to the tree of the apparitions, but finally he had to remain standing as he was wedged in by the crowd.

Almeida tried to estimate the number of people in the Cova, but gave up the attempt. It might be fifty thousand or a hundred thousand. The prayers of the crowd resounded over the vast space like the surge of the sea. Almeida made a few notes and impatiently lit a cigarette. Now another car drew up and stopped beside him. Almeida recognized his kindred spirit, the Prefect of Vila Nova de Ourém.

Letting down the window of his car, the editor called out to the Plumber, "Well! What do you think of this?"

"What should I say?" asked the Prefect, grinning. "There won't be any miracle in weather like this. It will be a fiasco for the clerical clique today."

"That's what I think, too."

"You must publish a good article about it with striking headlines! Your last one was far too tame."

"I kept it objective deliberately," replied Almeida, blowing a smoke ring from his cigarette. "I wanted everyone to know that the *Século* is unbiased. The day after tomorrow you will read another article that will satisfy you."

Meanwhile, in Aljustrel the two families were preparing to set out. The girls were wearing new dresses which a pious lady, the Baroness de Almeirim of Pombalinho, had given them. Lucia's was sky blue and Jacinta's white. Her weeping mother decorated Lucia's hair with a wreath of flowers.

"Don't be frightened, Mother!" the child begged her. "Nothing bad will happen to us. The Blessed Virgin will keep her promise."

"Ah, if it is the Mother of God who appears to you, why hasn't she worked a miracle long ago? She could have made a spring rise up as in Lourdes. But she has done nothing at all! What will be the end of it?"

"Stop lamenting, woman!" said Antonio dos Santos sharply. "It's time for us to be off. You had best stay at home."

"If they kill my daughter I shall die by her side," said the worried mother indignantly, facing her husband. "I'm going with her."

"That's right!" said Manuel Pedro. "I'm not frightened at all myself. I have no doubt whatsoever but that everything will be all right."

Olimpia was far less confident and was wringing her hands in despair.

At last they set out. The road was full of people, many of whom threw themselves on their knees before the children and asked for their intercession, begged their blessing, and bowed their heads as if in the presence of saints.

"Please don't do that!" Lucia begged them again and again. "Stand up and let us pass!"

But all this was only a feeble prelude to what was awaiting them at the Cova da Iria. The throng was so dense there that it seemed as though it would be impossible for them to reach the tree of the apparitions.

Luis, the village piper, at last found the children whom he had been awaiting anxiously. He had put on his military cap of the 6th Infantry Regiment in order to lend himself an air of importance.

"Let the children through!" he shouted loudly. "They are the children who have seen the Blessed Virgin!"

But this shout caused an even greater crush. Everyone wanted a glimpse of the children who had been favored by the Blessed Virgin. Manuel Pedro was jostled away from his little daughter's side.

"Father! Father!" cried the child desperately. "Don't push my father away like that!" she begged the people.

The farmer tried to reach the children again, but failed and was lost in the crowd. Luis promptly took the little girl up in his strong arms and ruthlessly forced his way through with her. The other children followed, led by Antonio dos Santos, who never let go of his daughter's hand. The small and slender Olimpia dropped behind and was swallowed up in the crowd, but her sister-in-law simply refused to allow herself to be pushed aside.

At last the little group appeared at the place of the apparitions. Some men whom Luis had mustered were waiting at the triumphal arch, on which lamps were lighted. They had sticks in their hands and protected the children from the crowd which was nearly suffocating them. The children were wet through and much disheveled. The new dresses were badly torn, and the wreaths of flowers were sitting awry over their veils. Francisco had lost his woolen cap; someone had taken it as a souvenir.

Maria-Rosa dos Santos and Maria Carreira took the two girls in hand and tried as much as possible to tidy them up. It was still pouring rain and must have been long past midday.

A priest was sitting on the low stone wall that surrounded the evergreen oak, reading his breviary under the protection of an umbrella. The children recognized the parish priest of Pôrto de Mos who had worried them so much with his questioning.

Dom Manuel shut his book noisily, pulled out his watch and said ironically, "It's long past midday now. The Blessed Virgin must be late, or perhaps she's not coming at all in such bad weather!"

"You must know, Father, that in our country it's not midday until half-past one," the piper informed him.

The priest became immersed in his breviary again. At

last he stood up and called out: "The hour is long past now! Go home, people! This is humbug and nonsense!" He tried to move the children away by force, but Luis and his companions prevented him.

"Anyone who wants to, can go, but I shall remain!" protested Lucia.

"After all, this is my land you're standing on, Father!" said her father angrily. "It's for me and nobody else to give orders here!"

Meanwhile, the crowd was becoming more restive from minute to minute, and the grumbling more audible.

"The priest is right!" somebody said. "The three young scamps deserve to have their heads cut off! Having us stand here getting drenched to the skin!"

"No!" someone else shouted. "It's the parents who are to blame. Making fools of us all! They should be put in prison!"

"It would have been better had we remained in Ourém!" someone else muttered. "We'd be having a nice plate of sausages and a good glass of wine there now!"

"Everyone to his fancy!" said the Plumber with a grin. "You will see what will happen, Senhor Almeida! The angry people will surely tear the children and their parents to pieces. Well, I wash my hands of it!"

"Yes, the hopes of the Church seem literally to be falling to the ground!" said the editor, very pleased. "This is the biggest flop they've had for the past hundred years."

Somewhere on the outskirts of the Cova a young couple were sitting in an automobile. They were on their honeymoon and had interrupted their journey to be present at the apparition.

"You might have thought of something better than dragging me here!" grumbled the young husband.

"Forgive me, darling!" said his wife with a sigh. "If you like we can drive on now!"

The husband got out to start up his car when he looked about him in amazement. What was this? The people all round were shutting their umbrellas although the rain had by no means abated. The thousands of people seemed all to be looking in one direction, but the young man was unable to see what was exciting their attention.

"We shall wait a little longer!" he said, getting into the car again.

"What on earth can be happening over there?" asked the young wife, shivering.

❧ 15 ❧

THE SUN DANCES
OVER FATIMA

The attitude of the disappointed crowd was becoming more and more menacing. Many people who had been saying the rosary only a short time before were now shaking their fists in the direction of the children.

"They should be hanged!" cried a hefty docker from Lisbon.

"There's a gallows ready there!" added another, pointing to the triumphal arch.

"They have deceived us, the little humbugs!" screeched a fishwife from Ourém. "Scratch their eyes out!"

"Do be calm!" a few wise people pleaded. "We have waited so long, another half hour won't make any difference now."

"No, not another minute!" cried others indignantly, trying to break through to the children.

"Now it's getting serious!" stammered Luis, turning pale. "In God's name! We'll soon show them what the 6th Infantry can do!" And with this he seized the docker by the collar and flung him back roughly. A general panic seemed inevitable.

"No violence, please!" cried the parish priest of Pörto de Mos, waving his arms to calm down the people. "Disperse quietly!"

"If a calamity happens here, Father, it will be your doing!" cried the village piper, resisting the angry assault with all his strength.

Francisco put a protecting arm around his weeping sister. Antonio dos Santos tried desperately to find a gap in the human wall through which he could carry away his little daughter.

Suddenly a woman stood up on the stone wall and cried in a loud voice, "Leave the children alone! They are innocent! I alone am to blame for all this!"

"Who is that woman?" people asked.

"She is Luisa, the bad woman!" the people of Fatima answered. "Perhaps she has really bewitched the children!"

"Seize the witch!" Ten, twenty hands caught hold of the outcast and dragged her to the ground by her dress and by her hair.

At that moment Lucia cried out in great excitement, "Did you see that! There was a flash of lightning in the distance! The Blessed Virgin is coming!"

"Where is she?" hundreds of voices cried.

"There! I see her!"

"Be careful, my child! Take great care that you are not mistaken," stammered Maria-Rosa, full of mortal anxiety lest the girl be injured.

"Yes, there she is!" the two other children now cried joyfully.

"She is there!" repeated Lucia, looking radiant. "Could you please close your umbrellas?" she asked the crowd.

A tremor, like the rustle of leaves, passed through the multitude. Men who had just been angrily shaking their fists now clasped their hands in prayer. Everywhere the umbrellas closed.

"The Blessed Virgin! The children see the Blessed Virgin!" The cry swept like a rushing wind over the Cova.

Every sign of fear had left the children's faces. Beaming with joy, they gazed at the Heavenly Being who was standing above the little evergreen oak, enveloped in a wondrous light. Her feet were resting on the wreath of flowers which Lucia and Jacinta had plaited in Valinhos. Everyone saw the silvery cloud which rose up around the tree like incense.

"Madam, who are you and what do you want of me?" they could hear Lucia asking.

And she answered, with the silvery tone of a bell:

"I am Our Lady of the Rosary. I have come to warn people to amend their lives."

Once more she exhorted the children to say the rosary every day. Then she added that the war would end soon and that the soldiers would be returning to their homes.

"I have so many favors to ask for others!" said Lucia, remembering the sick and those in trouble. The Blessed Virgin nodded.

"I know, my child!" she said. "Some will be healed and others will get the strength to bear their infirmities."

Then a shadow of grief passed over her face, and she said in a voice of supplication:

"People must not offend God any more, for He is already very much offended."

Then it seemed to the children as though the sky opened up in front of them. They no longer saw the Blessed Virgin alone; they also saw the Child Jesus in the glory of God the Father, and beside Him His foster father St. Joseph.

This marvelous apparition passed away, and now they saw the Blessed Virgin alone again. She raised her arm and pointed to the sun, then disappeared from the children's sight.

Lucia knelt in silence for a few moments, then she stood up and called out in a loud voice that resounded right over the valley:

"Oh, look at the sun!"

The rain had ceased suddenly. The dark clouds scattered in every direction, and the sun appeared like a large pale silver disc above the Cova da Iria.

"The sun! The sun!" cried thousands of voices. All eyes were turned toward the sky. No one was dazzled by the glare, which normally was quite blinding.

"It's the moon!" some people said. "It's not possible to look straight at the sun at this time of day!"

"No, no, it's the sun! There's a new moon now!" others protested. Then a cry of astonishment echoed over the Cova da Iria.

The sun trembled, then started to turn round on itself, at an ever-increasing speed, like a gigantic wheel of fire. Great beams of light—yellow, blue, red, green and violet— shot out from it in all directions. The pastures, the trees, the earth and the stones were illuminated by these magnificent colors. The spectators saw themselves, their clothes and their faces take on this succession of colors—the sevenfold colors of the rainbow—reflected from the sky.

At last the colors disappeared and the sun stood alone as before. But before a minute had passed, it started its fantastic motion again, more rapid and more colorful than the first time. This was repeated a third time. The clouds disappeared into the distance. Only a few little red-tinged clouds remained in the gold-tinted sky, and again the fantastic dance of the sun came to an end.

Then all of a sudden a cry of terror and alarm rose from the multitude. The sun had lost its place in the sky; it had started to move about! It became detached from the firmament, as it were, and was plunging down toward the earth!

"We are lost!" cried the people, panic-stricken. "It will crush us all!"

"My Jesus, have mercy on us!"

"I believe in God!"

"Forgive me my sins!"

Thousands fell on their knees, heedless of the mud which was ruining their clothes, and buried their faces in their hands.

And the sun danced! It was now as red as fire, and it danced a lively dance above the earth. At last, at last it stopped short in its incomprehensible round dance, returned to its normal position, and regained its usual noonday brilliance.

"A miracle! A miracle!" The cry rose up from all over the Cova. People who had never seen one another before fell into each other's arms, rejoicing, and laughing, and weeping. Astounded, the people felt their clothing. Only a few minutes before it had been raining in torrents, but now their clothing was as dry as if it had not rained at all. They were able to rub the dry dusty mud from their coats and dresses with their hands.

The young bridegroom, who had been about to drive away disappointed, threw himself on his knees on the muddy ground and repeated again and again:

"I believe! I believe! My God, forgive me my sins!"

"Milagre! Maravilha! A miracle, a miracle!" The cry resounded over the whole valley. Again the crowds surged toward the children. Men and women, who had been threatening them only a short time before, begged their forgiveness, weeping and sobbing. Tears were running down the weatherbeaten face of the docker who had been the first to threaten them. Full of anger, he looked about for the priest.

"The priest is to blame! The priest alone is to blame! It was he who set us against them!" he shouted over and over. But Dom Manuel had disappeared. Pale as death, he had slipped away, and vanished into the crowd.

Some women began to attend to Luisa, who had risen from the ground, her forehead bleeding and her clothing torn to shreds.

"She saved the children!" cried one of the villagers. "She drew the anger of the crowd on herself. She sacrificed herself to save the children."

"If anyone ever again dares to look down on her, I'll knock the teeth out of his head!" one man vowed grimly.

The children were once more in great danger from the general stampede. Lucia's parents had been pushed right away from her, and Maria-Rosa called in vain for her daughter. Finally a gigantic man, Dr. Carlos Mendés, a notary, took Lucia up on his shoulder and tried to carry her out of the crowd.

"Do penance! Do penance!" the little girl cried out over the people's heads. "The Mother of God wishes that you do penance! If you amend your lives the war will come to an end!"

The stalwart man who was carrying Lucia was buffeted from every side, and at last he stumbled and fell, and had to let go of the child. It was almost a miracle that Lucia got out of the crowd alive. She lost her wreath and veil; women cut off her long plaits of hair and tore pieces from her dress. If some intelligent men had not looked after her, she could hardly have escaped with her life.

Luis, the village piper, carried Jacinta in his strong arms. The child was almost on the point of fainting, and she laid her head, with its wreath of flowers, against his shoulder.

"Don't be afraid, little one!" the good man said again and again. "No one will do you any harm. You can trust an old African lion hunter to take care of you!"

"You mustn't tell lies! You mustn't tell lies, Luis!" said the little girl, smiling through her tears.

"No, of course not! That was definitely my last one!" the piper assured her.

Meanwhile a loud voice intoned a hymn to the Blessed Virgin, and soon the words "*Salve Regina! Mater misericordiae!*" resounded to the skies.

Arturo d'Oliveira Santos, the Prefect of Ourém, was standing beside his car, pale as death and trembling all over.

"What have you to say now, Senhor Almeida?" he inquired, disconcerted. "We have lost the game."

"Heaven is stronger than we are!" replied the editor.

"But what are you going to write now?" asked the agitated Prefect. "For God's sake, tell me what are you going to write?"

"Buy a copy of the *Século* the day after tomorrow and you can read it!" replied Almeida as he got into his car and tried to get through the crowd.

"It was a miracle!" he heard the people saying again and again as he passed. "We have seen a sign from heaven!"

Dr. Formigão returned to the rectory completely shaken by the happenings and found the parish priest in a state of great consternation. Dom Marcus had not left his house during the occurrences at the Cova da Iria, but he had seen the strange phenomena in the sky from his open balcony.

"Do you still doubt, my dear friend?" asked the Professor, after he had given the pastor a graphic description of what had happened.

"I don't know!" answered the priest. "I really don't know. We have to wait for the Church's verdict. A commission will have to investigate and examine the case. Yes, that will be best." He pinned all his hopes on a commission.

That same evening the Professor went to Aljustrel again to question the children. He found them in a singular state. Jacinta had escaped from the crowd more or less unhurt. Francisco, too, who was proud of having got away on his own feet, had not lost much except his wool cap and a few buttons off his jacket. But Lucia looked so odd without her plaits that the priest laughed outright.

"It's a shame the way they've been treated!" complained Maria-Rosa.

"You should be glad that they got home alive!" said the Professor.

"Well, it's a good thing that it's all over now!" said the mother with a sigh.

But the Professor shook his head thoughtfully and said, "Over? Not at all. I believe it has really only begun today."

In spite of all the excitement they had been subjected to, the children answered the Professor's questions calmly and with assurance. Again he found that all their answers agreed.

And so this remarkable day came to an end.

Over the heights of the Serra de Aire the red glow of the sunset faded away.

❦16❦

THE PREFECT IS ANNOYED

Arturo d'Oliveira Santos sat in his office looking over the reports of the incomprehensible happenings of the 13th of October. Although several days had passed, he had not yet recovered from his consternation, and he hoped to regain his mental equilibrium to some extent by reading the morning papers.

The Plumber was a man of boundless ambition. He had been appointed Prefect at the age of twenty-six, and he was looking forward to a highly successful career with the help of influential Freemason friends. But now he saw all his dreams for the future seriously endangered by the happenings in Fatima, in which he had played such an unfortunate part. Feeling very disgruntled he first took up the Lisbon Catholic daily, *A Ordem*. The clerics would be sure to sing a loud song of triumph, he thought, but as he read on the worried expression left his face. He had certainly not expected such moderation. After describing the "Dance of the Sun" the report continued:

"Why deny it? These occurrences, which we had never witnessed before, made a strong impression on us, and a powerful wave of faith filled the hearts of most of the crowd." But then the writer of the article went on to exhort the readers to the greatest reserve and prudence in the matter. They should wait and see if there might not be some natural explanation of the phenomena.

Greatly surprised, the Prefect looked back at the front page to make sure that he had not opened one of the Freemason papers instead of *A Ordem*. What then would the tone of the Liberal press be like?

The neutral paper, *O Primeiri de Janeiro* of Porto published a few lines about the events at the Cova da Iria but refrained from any criticism or comment.

Portugal, an organ of the Democratic Party, made game of the events in Fatima and, without any attempt to explain the facts, wrote: "Might not the dance of the sun be a clever advertisement in the American style for the Russian ballet which has just arrived in Lisbon?"

O Dia wrote in the same tone of feeble irony: "Vila Nova de Ourém possesses a sun of its own to illuminate it. This is a privilege which should not be tolerated any longer, particularly in a country where the streets of the capital were lighted by oil lamps until recently."

A Capital recommended that the fireworks enthusiast who had perpetrated this shocking carnival joke should be hunted down and arrested.

The Prefect searched in vain for his favorite paper, *O Mundo*. It turned out that the compositors had refused to print the article of the editor José do Vale and had gone on strike.

Finally the Prefect eagerly took up *O Século*, in which he found an article several columns long by his friend Avelino de Almeida. But the further he read the more he stared and the angrier his expression became. The big headlines ran:

"Astonishing Happenings—The Sun Dances at Midday in Fatima—The Apparition of the Blessed Virgin—A Sign from Heaven—Many Thousands Believe It Was a Miracle —War and Peace."

Filled with dismay the Prefect scanned the detailed account of the pilgrimage of tens of thousands to Fatima, of the patience of the crowds and the fervor with which they prayed, and of all the other happenings at the Cova da Iria. And then, with eyes that could scarcely believe what they saw, he continued to read:

"And now we see an extraordinary, unique spectacle, which is hard for anyone who has not witnessed it to believe. From far up in the village street where the vehicles are pressed together and where hundreds of people are standing about because they do not venture to walk through the muddy fields, the vast multitude is suddenly seen to turn toward the sun which has unexpectedly appeared in the now cloudless sky. It looks like a dull steel disc and one can look directly at it without any difficulty, for it does not dazzle the eyes. It looks somewhat like an eclipse of the sun. But now a loud roar is heard: 'A miracle!'

"A miracle! The sun is dancing! The sun is dancing! Before the astonished eyes of this crowd, whose attitude takes us back to Biblical times, and who, seized with fear and with bared heads look up at the blue sky where the sun trembles and makes abrupt movements never seen before and outside all cosmic laws. 'The sun begins to dance,' as the peasants so aptly put it. An old man is kneeling in prayer on the running board of an automobile. With his face turned toward the sun, he recites the Creed from beginning to end in a loud voice.

"Then the people commence asking each other if they have seen anything and if so what it was. Almost all testify that they have seen the sun trembling and dancing, others assert that they have even seen the smiling face of the Blessed Virgin and definitely maintain that the sun wheeled around in a circle like an artificial firework, that it swerved downward as if it were going to set the earth on fire with its light. Others assert that it turned different colors, one after another.

"It is nearly three o'clock in the afternoon.

"The sky is cloudless and the sun again stands there in the normal way and with its usual brilliance. But what of the shepherd children? Lucia, who has spoken to the Blessed Virgin, announces from the shoulder of a man who is carrying her that the war will soon be over and that the soldiers will be returning home. This news increases the general rejoicing.

"It was a sign from heaven!

"Let the experts give us their opinion about this fantastic dance of the sun, which today at Fatima has caused not only believers to cry out with joy, but also, as trustworthy people have assured me, freethinkers and other people without religious convictions, who had come to this moorland spot, already so celebrated."

The Prefect laid aside the paper angrily. So that was all —an enthusiastic report, not a word of criticism, no deductions, no reservations.

"Such a thing to read in an organ of the Freemasons!" cried the Prefect, banging the table with his fist. Then he stared in front of him for a long time, trying to think up a counterstroke.

One dark starless night the following week, a lorry with dimmed headlights drove from Santarém to Fatima. A dozen youths jumped out at the Cova da Iria and began their work of destruction. They knocked down the triumphal arch, stole the cross, the lamps and the candlesticks and used their axes to cut down the tree of the apparition. Finally they bound onto the lorry the oak tree they had cut down and drove quickly back to Santarém. The next day they held a procession there, carrying the objects they had stolen, and singing blasphemous songs and mock litanies. The pious people of Santarém looked on in helpless rage at this disgraceful exhibition, but they could not stop it. The Freemasons had provided for a strong police reinforcement under whose protection the diabolical game was carried on undisturbed.

The Catholics of Santarém sent an angry letter of protest to the Home Office in Lisbon, expressing their indignation at the insult to the Blessed Virgin, "whose name is the hope and strength of our soldiers who are fighting like heroes on the field of battle."

It was not only the faithful believers who condemned the desecration of the holy place. *O Século* joined in the general outcry, and wrote: "How could the authorities permit such an act and at the same time prohibit the Catholics from holding processions? They should remember that almost the entire Portuguese population are Catholics, and that their religious demonstrations do not hurt in any way the feelings of those who hold other beliefs."

The Plumber fumed with rage when he read this, and he wrote an angry letter to the freethinkers' central organization. He also ordered the Mayor of Fatima to prohibit all demonstrations or processions in the town.

"I can certainly forbid them!" said Senhor da Silva with

a sigh, when he read the official letter, "but how does the Prefect of Ourém think I can prevent them?"

"Yes, indeed, it would be hard for us to stop them," said Bernardo, the constable of Fatima. "We would require police reinforcements to do so."

Naturally the violation of the holy place caused terrible indignation in Fatima. The children's eyes filled with tears when they saw the destruction, but they had one consolation. In their rage the fellows from Santarém had cut down the wrong tree, and so the little evergreen oak of the apparitions had escaped destruction.

The triumphal arch was set up once more. It was now more beautiful than ever, and the prayers of the faithful consecrated anew the place which had been profaned; but no preparations were being made as yet to build the promised chapel to the Mother of God. This was not through lack of the necessary funds. The faithful had given not only money, but also large quantities of corn, olive oil, and other things. Maria Carreira faithfully guarded all the treasures.

But the consent of the parish priest was still lacking. Many people in Fatima were getting impatient and could not understand this delay. Some even suspected the good woman from Moita of enriching herself with the gifts that had been offered. The devout treasurer certainly suffered because of the suspicions, but she bore all the calumny with dignity.

The Prefect too began to investigate her. One day Manuel Carreira was summoned to Ourém. Knowing well why he was being called, he asked Farmer Marto's advice as to how he should behave.

"I think you will fare best if you pretend to be a fool,"

replied Ti Manuel artfully. "It's a good tip. I know that from my soldiering days."

"Very well," said the man from Moita, winking. "The Plumber will get nothing out of me."

The next day he appeared in the Prefect's office.

"What do you want?" asked the official peevishly.

"The Prefect sent for me. That's why I came—to know what he wants me for!" replied Manuel Carreira, twisting his cap in his hands with assumed nervousness.

"Where do you come from?"

"From Moita in the parish of Fatima."

"Then you must be Senhor Manuel Carreira?"

"That's right."

"You live near the Cova da Iria, don't you?"

"That's right."

"Do you go there often?"

"Yes."

"What do you do there?"

"The same as the others do."

"Have you seen the Blessed Virgin?"

"No."

"What do you go there for then?"

"The same as the others."

"What do the others say?"

"One person says one thing, the other, something else."

"People have given a lot of money there, haven't they?"

"I don't know."

"Have you not seen it, then? Don't you know anything about it?"

"Nothing at all."

"And who takes care of the money?"

"I don't know."

"You're a stupid fellow!"

"Yes, indeed, Senhor! Yes, indeed!"

"Clear out at once!" cried the Prefect, furious.

"With pleasure, Senhor Prefect. With pleasure!"

Manuel Carreira set his cap cockily on his head and trotted home, grinning to himself.

"Well, how did you make out?" Farmer Marto asked him.

"Splendidly! The Prefect almost burst with rage, but he got nothing out of me."

A few days later the Mayor of Fatima, accompanied by Bernardo, the constable, came to Moita to confiscate the money.

"It's no longer here!" Senhora Carreira explained, shrugging her shoulders.

"Where is it, then?"

"Stolen!"

"How has it been stolen?"

"I had it buried in the garden in a box. Thieves came and stole it."

"That's outrageous!" cried the Mayor, flying into a passion.

"I think so, too!" said the woman with a sigh. The Mayor looked at the policeman, perplexed, but the latter only shrugged his shoulders.

"Well, if someone has stolen the money from this woman, we cannot confiscate it," he said.

The Mayor went off in a very bad humor, while the constable trotted behind him, smiling.

Soon the news spread around Fatima that the money had been stolen. Some people came along indignantly and took Maria Carreira to task about it.

"Sometimes one can't manage without telling a lie!" she

replied calmly. The people understood and went away smiling.

The three children also heard the story. "You should not have told a lie!" said Lucia sadly when she met the treasurer shortly afterward at the place of the apparitions. "It's a sin to tell a lie! It's an offense against God!"

"But if I had told the truth the Mayor would have confiscated everything!" replied the woman, looking abashed into the little girl's angry eyes.

"But that would have been better than to have the money by telling a lie. You'll see, it will be a long time now before the chapel can be built."

"Perhaps you are right," replied Maria Carreira penitently.

❧ 17 ❧

THE GOLDEN ROAD

Remembering the Blessed Virgin's admonition that the three children should learn to read, the parents sent them to school at the beginning of the winter. It was a long way, so the children set out with their primers and slates every morning before sunrise. Lucia and even Jacinta learned eagerly and made good progress, but Francisco had great difficulty in keeping pace with them. During the last few months the boy had become strangely quiet, and the teacher often looked at him sympathetically when he saw him dreaming and pensive in class.

Francisco seemed to be living in another world. He knew that he was soon to die, and for that reason the prospect of mastering the alphabet and the multiplication table was not very attractive. In his thoughts he was already wandering along toward heaven.

Again and again strangers who had come to Fatima to see the children spoke to them on their way to school.

"Well, my boy, what are you going to be?" two ladies asked Francisco one day, trying to make the silent boy speak. The boy only shrugged his shoulders.

"Would you like to be a carpenter?"

"No, Senhora!"

"Or a soldier?"

"No, Senhora!"

"Or a doctor? Perhaps you'd like to go to the University?"

"No, Senhora!"

"Now I know what you would like to be!" said the lady, as an idea occurred to her. "You surely want to be a priest. You would like to say Mass, and hear confessions, and preach, wouldn't you?"

"No, Senhora! I don't want to become a priest!"

"But what would you like to be, then?"

"I don't want to be anything. I want to die and go to heaven!" said the boy looking at the ladies solemnly with his brown eyes.

Greatly moved, they went their way. People often came to the children with all kinds of requests. They begged for their intercession, and the three children brought the troubles of others to the church and entrusted them to Our Lord in the Tabernacle and to His Blessed Mother. And the prayers of the children were seldom left unanswered. Sick people were cured, a prodigal son who had been roaming the world returned home, a father who was being sent to the front leaving a sick child behind him was inexplicably exempted.

One morning Lucia's eldest sister, Maria dos Anjos, who had been married shortly before, waylaid the children on their way to school to tell them that her brother-in-law had been arrested on a serious charge and was to be tried that same day.

"Pray that he may be proved innocent!" she begged the children, in tears.

As the three were passing the church, Francisco said, "You go on to school! I shall pray here for the accused man until you come back!"

"But what will the teacher say?" protested Jacinta.

"I think this is more important than school," replied the boy firmly.

When the two girls returned from school and went to the church, Francisco whispered to Lucia, "Tell your sister that her brother-in-law will be acquitted!"

"How do you know that?" asked his cousin.

"I simply know he will!"

And actually the young man did return very soon from Ourém, his innocence proved.

The children loved to take their flocks to Valinhos because they enjoyed the solitude there. But Francisco, who used to like so much playing with the others, wanted to be still more solitary. He climbed up into the trees and sometimes remained for hours in the branches of an oak tree.

"Come down and we'll eat our lunch!" Lucia called up to him one day.

"You two take it! I'm not hungry!" came the answer.

"But what are you doing up there?"

"I'm thinking!"

"What are you thinking about?"

"I'm thinking of God!"

"But we'll say the rosary together when we've eaten!" Jacinta reminded him.

"When you're ready to pray, call me and I'll come down!"

After Christmas the wonderful time of preparation for their First Holy Communion began for the brother and sister. The parish priest held the class in the church. Jacinta put her whole heart into learning and her brother too was overjoyed at the thought of the great day that he had looked forward to for so long. But during instructions he became lost in thought again and again, and when the priest questioned him he gave such silly answers in his confusion that Jacinta often felt ashamed of him.

"Pay attention!" the priest said to him repeatedly. But that did not help, for all Francisco's thoughts were already on the golden road to heaven.

Shortly before the longed-for day, the parish priest sent for Farmer Marto and told him that Jacinta was well prepared, but unfortunately he could not allow Francisco to make his First Holy Communion that year because he had not learned the lessons adequately.

"What on earth is the matter with the boy?" he asked the farmer.

"I don't know what's the matter with him either," said the farmer with a sigh. "He has somehow changed recently, and it often seems to me that only his body is here in this world, and his soul is somewhere else."

When the boy was told the sad news, he was intensely grieved, and Jacinta tried in vain to console him. It was only when she assured him that she would pray for him with all her heart when she received Holy Communion that his eyes brightened again.

"It's a great sorrow for you that the priest won't permit you," Jacinta said to him. "But offer it to the Blessed Virgin for the conversion of sinners and for the Holy Father! What a wonderful sacrifice you will be offering her! Ah, I almost envy you!"

"You are right!" replied Francisco and went away in silence.

The little girl's soul was filled with a heavenly joy on the day when she at last received the Bread of Angels for the first time.

That summer there was great suffering all over the Serra de Aire. A severe epidemic called Spanish influenza spread from house to house, and young and old fell ill and had to lie in bed. Everyone in the Marto family contracted the illness except Manuel Pedro, but little Francisco had the worst case of all. He suffered terribly, but he patiently offered all his sufferings to God.

"If only Our Saviour is no longer sad!" he whispered almost to himself when he was tortured with fever and nearly dying of thirst. "If I can only console Our Lord by this!"

His sufferings lasted all through the autumn, but about Christmas he grew a little better. He was even able to go with his brothers and sisters on a fine sunny day to their favorite haunt, the cave of Cabeço.

"Now it won't be long until you're quite well again!" his relatives and friends said encouragingly. But the boy always shook his head and said, "No, I shan't get well again." His grave tone and sad expression almost frightened those about him.

"I'll give the Blessed Virgin as many kilos of wheat as your weight if you get well!" his godmother promised him one day.

"You can keep your wheat, Auntie!" said the boy, smiling. "I'm going to heaven!"

Toward the end of February he became very ill again.

"Have you a lot of pain?" Lucia, who visited him every day, asked him.

"My head hurts me," the sick boy admitted, "but I'll bear it all to console Jesus."

All kinds of people, friends and strangers, came to the little house to visit the sick child and to marvel at his patience. They often brought their own requests to him and told him of their troubles. A mother complained that her husband had banished their only son from the house on account of something he had done, and she greatly wished for a reconciliation.

"I'll soon be in heaven!" said Francisco seriously. "Then I'll ask the Blessed Virgin for this favor for you."

He became weaker from day to day. One day he asked his sister Teresa to fetch Lucia, because he wanted to talk to her about something important.

"I must go to Confession today," he confided to his cousin. "Please help me to examine my conscience! Tell me what wrong I have done!"

"Sometimes you have not obeyed your mother when she called you in from play!" Lucia reminded him.

"Yes, that is true!" said the boy sadly. "Can't you think of anything else? Then please call Jacinta!"

The little sister thought very seriously, then she said, "You took money from Father to buy a mouth organ. And you threw stones at the boys from Boleiros with the other Aljustrel boys!"

"Yes, I'm very sorry for that," replied the boy, penitently.

On the 3rd of April, 1919, Francisco received Holy Communion from the hands of the parish priest. Although he was tortured by raging thirst all the previous night, he would not take a drop of water.

He was full of joy on receiving the Heavenly Bread.

When the priest had left the house, the dying boy said to Jacinta and Lucia, "Now I shall go to heaven. When I'm there I'll ask Jesus and Mary to take you two to paradise soon. Say the rosary once more near me!" he whispered, and joined in as well as he could.

The day passed. The mother watched by her son's bedside that night. Toward six o'clock in the morning he raised himself up a little, pointed to the door and whispered, "Do you see that beautiful light there?" After a while he said, "Now I don't see it any more!" Then he sank back on his pillow, exhausted. Soon afterward he breathed his last. He passed away from this world quietly and with a smile on his lips.

"Farewell until we meet in heaven!" Olimpia whispered to him through her tears.

Then she closed the child's eyes for his last sleep.

A lark rose up into the sky over Valinhos and hovered about singing joyfully in the golden light of the spring morning.

❧18❧

A LONELY DEATH

Jacinta knew that she too would soon have to die, and with childish seriousness she prepared for her last hour. During the short time which still remained to her, she did all she could to atone for the sins of mankind, and she was consumed with a longing for sacrifice and suffering. The expression of her normally lively eyes became more and more strange and thoughtful. She often looked as though she were looking toward some vast, distant country.

One day, as she was sitting thoughtfully on one of the rocks at Cabeço, the landscape seemed suddenly to change in an extraordinary way. The peaceful Valinhos, on which her sheep were grazing in the summer sunlight, changed before her astonished eyes and gave place to a strange country she had never seen, with villages and small towns.

Then from somewhere in the distance came a strange roaring and rumbling, a crackling and flashing as if the whole sky were tumbling down to the earth in the midst of a thousand thunderstorms. Storm raged through all the streets with the flames of a fire; churches and houses crashed down in the blazing embers. Sparks flashed up toward the flaming sky, and through the raging hell a huge steel monster rolled with fire-spitting funnels. And the earth trembled, groaned, and cried out as from a thousand mouths. Then quiet fell again. The flames were now distant, like the red glow of evening.

Snow fell from the sky and covered the countryside like a huge winding sheet, and the frozen branches of broken-down trees blocked many roads. Human beings staggered about, exhausted by cold and hunger, fell down groaning, then picked themselves up again and dragged themselves on for a bit with swaying steps—people with tired, hollow eyes, men young and old with miserable bundles in their stiff hands, women with little children in their arms. The ghostly procession became bigger and bigger, swelled to an overflowing stream, like an avalanche of dead.

Jacinta uttered a cry and buried her face in her hands to banish the terrible sight.

"What's the matter?" cried Lucia, hurrying up to her, alarmed.

"It's the war, the war!" stammered the little one, as if waking from a bad dream.

"But the war was over long ago. There's peace!"

"No, it's another war! A war which is going to come! Didn't you see the houses on fire, and all the streets and roads and fields full of suffering people? They were weeping with hunger and cold."

"But look around you! It's still summer and everything is peaceful and quiet!"

Jacinta remained silent for a long time, then she whispered, "When I go to heaven I will pray that the war won't come to Portugal."

Another time, when Lucia was looking for wild bees' nests in a bed of shrubs, Jacinta cried out in great distress:

"Did you see the Holy Father, Lucia? I saw him in a great big house. He was kneeling down before a table, with his face in his hands, weeping. There were a lot of people outside. Some of them were throwing stones, others were swearing and shouting very wicked words. . . . The poor Holy Father! We must pray for him."

A few days after that she saw the Pope again; this time he was in a great cathedral where many candles were burning in front of magnificent altars, and he was dedicating the whole world to the Immaculate Heart of Mary.

"Oh, it was beautiful, Lucia! I cannot tell you how beautiful!" she told her cousin, radiant with happiness.

The child's thin little face was glowing like fire. On the way home she was seized with dizziness, and Lucia had to hold her up. Her heart was beating furiously, and she suddenly felt a piercing pain.

Olimpia was horrified when she saw her daughter staggering in the door. She put her to bed at once and prepared a hot drink to relieve the fever. A few days later the doctor diagnosed severe pleurisy. Jacinta suffered unspeakably, but she was glad that she now had a greater sacrifice to offer to God.

Lucia visited her every day and brought her flowers from the Cabeço—the wild lilies and peonies which Jacinta loved so much. One day Lucia brought her a specially happy piece of news.

"Just imagine!" she said, beaming with joy. "They're going to build the chapel at the Cova da Iria."

"How wonderful!" cried the sick child, her eyes shining. And it was as Lucia said. The parish priest had at last given up opposing the plan, and though he did not support the building of the chapel, he had said at last: "Do as you wish!" That was enough for Maria Carreira, and she began the long-planned work at once. They built a little sanctuary, but since no decision had yet been taken by the Church, it could not be consecrated by a priest.

When Jacinta was somewhat better she was taken there in a covered horse trap so that she too could pray in the chapel.

That same summer death claimed a victim in the Santos' home, too. Antonio the father was stricken with the influenza and went to bed, never to get up again. Full of repentance, he prepared for his last hour. On the 31st of July, 1919, he passed away.

Soon afterward Maria-Rosa herself fell seriously ill. When she was at the brink of death, she called her daughter Lucia and said to her, "If what you say is true, then go to the Cova da Iria and pray there!"

The girl obeyed joyfully. When she arrived home, her mother was already much better. In three days she was able to get up. Her recovery seemed almost a miracle, yet she still remained half unbelieving.

Not long after, Lucia found her cousin Jacinta in a state of great excitement.

"I've seen the Blessed Virgin again!" she told her joyfully. "She told me that I shall have to go into two hospitals yet, but not to get well, only to suffer."

She offered up all her pain with touching patience. Although they made her terribly sick, she took the milk or the soup her mother brought her. If the good Olimpia had only known how she tormented her child with these!

At last the doctor ordered Jacinta's removal to the hospital at Vila Nova de Ourém. What grief it was for the little girl to leave home! But she bore this sacrifice bravely, too. Her mother visited her often, but the sick child was almost more pleased when Lucia came to her bedside from time to time.

"I went to Holy Communion this morning!" Lucia told her cousin one Sunday.

"Oh, how wonderful!" cried the little girl. "What do you think, Lucia? Will we be able to go to Holy Communion in heaven? If so, I shall do so every day."

Her condition did not improve in the hospital. The wound was still suppurating, and the changing of the bandages was terribly painful.

"Have you a lot of pain?" Lucia asked her one day.

"Yes, the wound hurts a lot," admitted Jacinta. "But don't tell anyone, not even Mother! It would only make her sad!"

Even in the hospital Jacinta was not spared the visits of strangers. People came to her with so many requests that her head often ached.

"Ah, if only I could run away from them and hide, as I used to do!" she sometimes said. "But I shall offer this cross to our Saviour, too."

At the end of August she was brought home once more. She was glad to be able to have intimate talks with her cousin again. But how seldom they were alone! More and more visitors came to see her. Neighbors came and were quite happy to sit knitting silently by her bedside.

"One feels so happy near her!" they said. The little room was often swarming with children, and Jacinta did not rebuff them although their noise hurt her.

During many nights, when the sick child was tortured with fever, Olimpia sat by her bed, cooling her burning forehead and giving her soothing drinks. Jacinta often noticed that her mother's eyes were full of tears.

"Don't cry, Mother!" she would say with a smile. "I'm quite happy, and I'll soon be going to heaven and will pray a lot for you."

But sometimes she lay for a long time just looking before her, deep in thought.

"What is it, child?" her mother asked one day.

"Ah, nothing!" Jacinta replied. But later she confided her secret sorrow to her cousin.

"I've a lot to think about!" she said. "About Our Lord and His Blessed Mother, and sinners, and the war that is to come. So many will have to die. So many homes will be destroyed; so many priests will be killed. What misery! If people stopped offending God, the war would not come, and so many people would not go to hell."

"Be quiet and try to sleep!" said Lucia.

But the little girl shook her head, and drawing her cousin closer to her, said: "I am soon going to heaven. And you, when you see the light in the night which the Blessed Virgin told us about, you too must flee up to us!"

"But one cannot simply flee to heaven like that!" replied Lucia, smiling.

"That's true!" said Jacinta. "But still don't be afraid! In heaven I shall pray for you, and for the Holy Father, and for Portugal, that the war may not come here, and for all priests, too!"

Toward the end of the year, the Blessed Virgin told the little girl that she would soon be going to a big house in Lisbon.

"I know I shall die there," Jacinta told her cousin. "I have suffered so much. Now I am to die alone—quite alone!"

In January a famous doctor from Lisbon came to see her, accompanied by a priest. Dr. Lisboa examined her case and said, shaking his head, "She will not get well here. She must be taken to Lisbon—she will be cured there."

"How will that help?" said Manuel Pedro despondently. "The little one doesn't want to get well. She wants to go to heaven!"

But in the end he agreed, and all preparations were made for the journey to Lisbon. Jacinta said farewell to the dear familiar places of her childhood. Her family took her once more to the Cova da Iria, on a donkey, and she said the rosary in the tiny chapel. The next day she said a last good-by to her father and brothers and sisters.

"Come home to us soon!" stammered Manuel, who was hardly able to hold back his tears.

"Yes, home to heaven!" said the child. "We'll all see one another again there."

When Lucia embraced her for the last time, Jacinta said in a weak voice, "We shall not see each other again in this world! Pray for me until I go to heaven! Then, when I'm there, I'll pray for you. Don't tell the secret to anyone, even if they should kill you! Love Jesus and the Immaculate Heart of Mary and continue to make many sacrifices for sinners!"

Then her father lifted her up onto the oxcart, her mother got up, too, and her brother Antonio drove them to the station at Chão de Maças. As they left the village they found Luis, the piper, standing waiting for her.

"Get well, little one, and come home in good health!" he called out to her.

"Oh, Luis, I'm going to heaven!" said Jacinta, shaking her head.

"Then don't forget me altogether!" begged the good fellow. "And sometimes if you have nothing else to do in heaven, ask God to forgive me my thousand sins."

"I shall not forget you, Luis," the little girl replied gravely.

"Then drive on! I'll send a farewell greeting after you!"

And as the cart rumbled off, Luis played Jacinta's favorite tune on his pipes.

"Listen, Mother!" cried the little girl, beaming. "Do you hear it? How beautiful, oh, how beautiful!" Then she hummed the melody:

> Sing my tongue the Saviour's glory,
> Of His Flesh the mystery sing;
> Of the Blood, all price exceeding,
> Shed by our immortal King,
> Destined, for the world's redemption,
> From a noble womb to spring.
>
> Of a pure and spotless Virgin
> Born for us on earth below,
> He, as man with man conversing,
> Stayed, the seeds of truth to sow;
> Then He closed in solemn order
> Wondrously His life of woe.
>
> Down in adoration falling,
> Lo, the Sacred Host we hail;
> Lo! o'er ancient forms departing
> Newer rites of grace prevail;
> Faith, for all defects supplying,
> Where the feeble senses fail.
>
> To the Everlasting Father,
> And the Son who reigns on high,
> With the Holy Ghost proceeding
> Forth from each eternally,
> Be salvation, honor, blessing,
> Might, and endless majesty.

The solemn melody died away in the distance. In the clear brightness of the winter day, they passed by the meadows and fields and all the loved homeland with its silver, shimmering olive trees, its hills and mountains, its little whitewashed houses, and the great wings of the windmills.

With tear-filled eyes Jacinta gazed for the last time on the glorious Serra de Aire, and in the calm of her heart she bade a last farewell to her native wilds.

When they arrived at the station, Antonio said good-by and returned home with the cart. Then the express train, which was to take Jacinta away from her native place forever, rushed into the station. Freezing with cold, Jacinta and her mother entered the carriage and the train pulled out. It seemed an endless time until they arrived at the principal station of Lisbon. A good friend of theirs had asked someone to meet them, and the little girl was wearing a white band on her arm as a sign of identity. But no one noticed her in the great crowd.

Her mother wandered helplessly about the big station, carrying her poor suitcase in her hand, until at last someone showed her the waiting room. Then the gentleman who was to meet them arrived. He had been unavoidably delayed, but now he took them in a car to the orphanage of Our Lady of the Miracles, where Jacinta was to stay for a time.

Her mother, weeping bitterly, embraced her for the last time and said, "Come home to us soon!"

"Yes, I shall be going home soon!" replied Jacinta. She was not thinking of the poor home in Aljustrel, however, but of heaven.

Mother Maria Purificata Godinho looked after the sick child with motherly love, and the little girl's patience in her suffering edified everyone. Jacinta's greatest consolation now was the fact that she was living under the same roof as Our Lord. Her health improved and she was able to get up sometimes and visit the chapel, where she prayed before the Tabernacle with touching fervor.

"What is the name of the street we are living on, Madrinha?" she asked Mother Godinho one day. This kind lady was called "Godmother" by the children in the home.

"It is the Via das Estrelas—the street of the stars, my child!"

"Oh, how lovely!" smiled Jacinta. "I would like to die here. Then I would go to heaven by the street of the stars!"

One day she was actually well enough to go to Confession in the nearby church. She returned to the home radiant with happiness and said, "Oh, what a good priest, what a good priest! He said such nice things to me!" Then she added in an unhappy tone: "But there were people chattering in the church. People shouldn't talk in church! Do tell the Cardinal, Minha Madrinha, that people shouldn't talk in church! The Blessed Virgin does not like it. You will tell the Cardinal, won't you?"

"Yes, my child, I certainly shall, as soon as I see him!" Mother Godinho assured her.

Jacinta remained for two weeks in that friendly home, then she became very ill and the doctor who had examined her in Fatima was informed of her state.

"Why was I not called sooner?" he asked reproachfully. "She must go to the hospital at once!"

"I know they are going to operate on me!" Jacinta said to Mother Godinho when the doctor had gone away. "But it isn't any use. The Blessed Virgin has told me that I am going to die, and I already know the day and the hour."

"Oh, no, my treasure, you're going to get well!" Mother Godinho protested.

"No, no, I'm going to heaven!" the little one insisted. "But tell me, Minha Madrinha, is there a chapel in the hospital, too?"

"No, my child, the Dona Stefania Hospital is a secular hospital, but there are very clever doctors there."

"Doctors cannot help me, and if Jesus does not live there, I would rather die here."

However, she had to give way to the wishes of the doctors and she was taken to the hospital on the feast of the Purification.

"Purulent pleurisy of the left cavity of the chest, caries of the seventh and eighth rib on the same side," they wrote on her chart.

On Tuesday, the 10th of February, she was operated on. Two ribs were removed, and this left a wound the breadth of a hand. It was not possible to give her a chloroform anesthetic because she was too weak, so she only had a local one. Her suffering was indescribable.

"I'm very sorry to have to hurt you," said the surgeon.

The little girl only shook her head bravely and gasped, "We all have to suffer if we want to go to heaven."

She bore everything with resignation. The changing of the dressings hurt her terribly, too, but she was extraordinarily patient. Mother Godinho, who visited her every day, always found her inexplicably merry.

"Why should I be sad since the Blessed Virgin is soon going to take me to heaven?" she said again and again, smiling.

The operation seemed to be successful, and Dr. Lisboa wrote reassuringly to Aljustrel. Jacinta alone knew how mistaken he was. She soon became so weak that a priest was called on the 20th of February.

"I'm going to heaven today!" the little girl told him with complete conviction. "Please give me the Last Sacraments!"

"Oh, there's no need to hurry!" said Dr. Pereira dos Reis, the parish priest of the Church of the Holy Angels. Nevertheless he heard her Confession and anointed her.

"I shall bring you Holy Communion in the morning," he said as he left her.

"Oh, please don't wait until morning, Father! Bring me Holy Communion today, for I shall die tonight," begged the child.

"It will certainly be time enough in the morning!"

Mother Godinho came again in the evening to see how she was.

"I shall die in a few hours," Jacinta told her. "I shall have to die alone. They have not even brought Our Lord to me!"

"Our Lord is always in your heart!" the lady said consolingly.

"Yes, you are right, Minha Madrinha," replied Jacinta slowly.

"I shall come back again in the morning," Mother Godinho promised.

"I shall only see you again in heaven!" replied the little girl definitely.

The hours passed slowly. From time to time a nurse who was on night duty looked in at the door, but the little girl lay so quiet and peaceful that the nurse did not think there was any danger. When the nurse came into the room again at about half-past ten, Jacinta was already dead.

The Madonna had kept her promise and taken her to

heaven. Jacinta was placed in her coffin wearing her white First Communion dress with the blue belt. When the news spread that the little seer of Fatima was dead, the faithful of the capital thronged the hall of the Brotherhood of the Blessed Sacrament, where she was laid out. From the open coffin came a perfume like the odor of spring flowers.

Four days later the body was brought to Vila Nova de Ourém, where it was laid in the vault of a noble family. In September, 1935, she was reinterred in the cemetery of Fatima. When the coffin was opened, the child's body was found to be completely incorrupt.

On the 1st of May, 1951, her body was once more reinterred, this time in the wonderful new Basilica of Fatima, where she and her brother Francisco were laid in their final resting place, one at each side of the high altar, in the presence of their parents and of an immense concourse of people. A year previously the Church had introduced the cause of the beatification of the two children.

❧ 19 ❧

THE WAY INTO SILENCE

Now Lucia was alone. Just as before, she went about her daily work in silence, learned to read and write at school, minded her mother's little flock of sheep, and spent her leisure hours meditating and praying at Cabeço or in the Chapel of the Apparitions in the Cova da Iria.

The faithful of Portugal made pilgrimages in increasing numbers to the sanctuary of the Blessed Virgin. The Prefect of Vila Nova de Ourém and also the Government in Lisbon, tried in vain to stop the ever-increasing pilgrimages. When a large reinforcement of police proved ineffective, they thought of calling in the army to enforce their prohibition.

On the 13th of May, 1920, large detachments of cavalry and infantry cordoned off all roads leading to the Cova da Iria. Every vehicle going to Fatima was stopped, but the pilgrims, carrying crosses and banners, broke through the enemy lines and forced an entry into the hallowed place. The soldiers, who at heart were believing Catholics themselves, allowed themselves to be overcome, and many of them joined the pilgrims and said the rosary with them at the sanctuary. The same day a statue of the Blessed Virgin was carried to the Cova da Iria on top of an oxcart laden with hay and solemnly set up in the little chapel for the people to pray before.

One of the military officers who had been instructed to cordon off the holy place said to Dr. Formigão, who was also in Fatima that day: "If you only knew how much I dislike being here, Father! I have to obey orders, but believe me, I am furious about it. I believe in the apparitions myself, and I don't see why these poor people should be prevented from coming here to pray. Our Lady of Fatima saved the life of my sister."

Lucia followed all these happenings, full of silent sympathy. Of course she herself was again and again the center of general attention. She simply could not escape the attentions of all the strangers, many of whom showed her the respect due to a saint.

One day a new bishop, José Alves Correia da Silva, was appointed to the diocese of Leiria, to which Fatima belonged, and which had been without a bishop during all the time of persecution. The bishop, who had spent a long time in prison during the years of revolution, had deep devotion to the Blessed Virgin and dedicated his bishopric to her on the feast of the Assumption, ten days after coming to the diocese. He carefully studied all the accounts of the apparitions in the Cova da Iria, and one of the first journeys he took was to Fatima.

Dom Marcus had been transferred to another parish some time before at his own request. He had been replaced by his cousin, Dom Agostinho Ferreira, a zealous and prudent priest, who firmly believed in the apparitions. In his presence the bishop questioned Lucia, the sole survivor of the three young seers.

After listening to her story with deep emotion, he said to her, "Would it not be better for you to go away from Fatima? You will never be left in peace here."

"Do you mean that I should go away from here?" stammered the girl, alarmed.

"Only if you want to, and if your mother agrees; I cannot force you to do so. But I would place you in a religious house where you would have quiet and find the true peace of God, which you certainly cannot have here with this great rush of pilgrims about."

"Yes, my Lord, do what you think best with me!" replied Lucia submissively.

And so it was that she left her home the following spring and went to live in the orphanage of the Sisters of St. Dorothy in Vilar, near Porto.

With a sorrowful heart she said her last Hail Mary at the sanctuary of the Blessed Virgin, bade farewell to her mother, relatives and friends, paid a last visit to the cemetery in Fatima and adorned Francisco's little grave with flowers. A few days later she knocked at the door of her new home.

The Reverend Mother looked with surprise at the girl who appeared before her in her rough, strong shoes, carrying her belongings in a miserable little bundle. So this simple peasant child was supposed to have seen the Blessed Virgin? Perhaps it was really all deception and deceit? The Church had not yet given her verdict on the apparitions, and there were still many priests in the country who did not believe in them at all. In any case the greatest caution seemed indicated.

"What have you learned, my child?" asked the nun finally.

"*Não sei!* I don't know!" stammered Lucia, intimidated.

"Well, what did you used to do at home?"

"I minded the sheep and spread dung in the fields!"

"Unfortunately we have neither fields nor sheep here," sighed the Reverend Mother. "But you can make yourself useful in the kitchen. You will be able to learn something there at least. And besides you can attend the school with the other girls."

"Yes, Reverend Mother!" replied Lucia.

"And one thing more! You are strictly forbidden to speak about the apparitions that you allege you have seen. From now on your name is no longer to be Lucia but Maria das Dores—Maria of the Sorrows. If anyone asks you where you come from, say that you come from near Lisbon. That is no lie!"

"Yes, Reverend Mother!"

"You are not to go for walks with the other pupils, and you are not to tell them why you are not allowed to do so!"

"Yes, Reverend Mother!"

Then Lucia had to put on the dark school uniform with the black-and-white checked collar.

She remained in Vilar for four years. No one except the Reverend Mother knew who she was, what her real name was, or where she came from. Lonely and silent, she went about her duties obediently.

Lucia had not learned much in the short time she had been attending school in Fatima, so it was difficult for her to follow the lessons, and the other pupils often jeered at the dull peasant girl who kept so aloof and often gave such stupid answers.

She suffered terrible homesickness. Her thoughts returned constantly to her home, to Francisco's and Jacinta's graves, to the silent hills of Valinhos and to the Chapel of the Blessed Virgin in the Cova da Iria.

She alone knew nothing of what was happening at the place of the apparitions. The whole world heard with indignation of the bomb outrage which had destroyed the Chapel of the Blessed Virgin on the night of the 6th of February, 1922, of its rebuilding and of the great procession of atonement which the Catholics of Portugal made to Fatima on the thirteenth of the following May, and of the processions of pilgrims that soon had begun to come from all over the world to the Cova da Iria.

Although even her mother in Aljustrel kept her daughter's whereabouts secret, an enterprising newspaper reporter succeeded in discovering where she was. But when he went to see her, he was told, "No one named Lucia lives here. In fact, there is no one here from Fatima."

It wasn't until her third year in Vilar she learned that the Bishop of Leiria had appointed a commission to investigate the apparitions. Some priests came to her and interrogated her confidentially about the happenings there. Then again for a long time she heard nothing at all and suffered tormenting uncertainty about all that was occurring in Fatima.

"Reverend Mother, I should like to become a Sister of St. Dorothy," she said one day very timidly to the Superior.

"But why would you like to?" asked the latter.

"Because I could go to the chapel more often then," replied Lucia hesitantly.

"You are too young as yet. You must wait some time."

Lucia accepted this decision humbly and did not bring up the subject again.

A year later the Reverend Mother asked her, "You're

not thinking any more about becoming a nun, are you?"

"Oh, yes, I'm always thinking of it. It is what I want with all my heart."

"Very well, then, you may enter the convent."

Lucia made her novitiate in Tuy, a Spanish town on the Portuguese frontier. On the 2nd of October, 1926, she received the religious habit. Two years later she took her first vows with a happy heart and full of the spirit of sacrifice, taking the name of Sister Maria das Dores. Henceforth her whole life was to be a consecrated chalice, as it were, filled anew each day with the wine of sacrifice. How happy she was to make the renunciations which the religious life demanded of her!

After she was professed she was given the office of sacristan. One day a Portuguese priest, who did not know her name, asked her about the famous Sister Maria of the Sorrows.

"Famous?" repeated the sacristan hesitantly.

Aha, the little nun is jealous, thought the priest. Then, facetiously seeking to irritate her more, he added, "She's certainly famous. All Portugal is talking about her. What kind of a person is she?"

"She's just a nun like the others or like myself! We're all the same!"

The sacristan is not only jealous, but crazy with conceit, decided the priest. And he left the convent without ever suspecting that he had been speaking to Lucia.

On another occasion she accompanied a sister to Valença, a village at the other side of the frontier, to make some purchases. Just as they had crossed the Minho, the river which divides Spain from Portugal, two ladies came up to them and asked, "Are you Sisters of St. Dorothy?"

"Yes, we are."

"From Tuy?"

"Yes!"

"We are going over there to see Lucia, the seer from Fatima. She's in Tuy, isn't she?"

"Oh, no, she's in Portugal!" replied Maria das Dores. And that was true at the moment.

"What a pity! Then we have been misinformed," said the ladies regretfully, turning back.

"Is Lucia really supposed to be in our convent?" the other sister asked, quite unsuspecting.

"She is definitely not in Tuy now!" Lucia assured her, laughing to herself at the success of her ruse.

On the 3rd of October, 1934, Lucia took her final vows. Now she was dedicated to Our Lord and His Blessed Mother forever. And the day brought another great joy with it, for her mother attended the ceremony, having received permission to visit her daughter again after so many years.

Maria-Rosa brought with her a big bouquet of wild flowers from Valinhos. Lucia was unable to hold back her tears when she took in her hands the flowers which brought back so many happy memories. But then she quietly carried them to the chapel and laid them before the picture of the Blessed Virgin.

And what wonderful news she learned about her native place. After lengthy investigation the Bishop had confirmed the genuineness of the apparitions and solemnly announced the fact. He had also bought from her mother the piece of land on which the chapel stood.

"And just imagine, child," the peasant woman continued, "they had great need of water for the large number of pilgrims who now come to Fatima. When they were sinking a cistern at the Cova da Iria, they came on a powerful spring. No one had ever thought that there could be a spring in the limestone. But now it has been found, and there's plenty of good, fresh water, enough for thousands of people. They have also erected Stations of the Cross, and an immense Basilica is being built. The Bishop himself has laid the cornerstone. And there have been many miraculous cures there. I don't know how many people have been cured—blind, and lame, and consumptives."

There was no end to the news. Lucia listened attentively, then she clasped her hands as if in prayer.

"And you, Mother? Do you also believe now?" she asked at last.

"Yes, now that the Church has confirmed it, I can no longer doubt."

"That is the most beautiful gift you could give me!" said Lucia, deeply moved.

She asked a hundred other questions, and her mother willingly told her all she wanted to know.

The Plumber of Ourém had long since lost his position as Prefect and still bore a grudge against the Blessed Virgin for having destroyed all his plans for the future.

"And what about Luis, the village piper?"

"He's the same old rogue as ever, and he sent his greetings to you."

Her mother's visit had brought back her childhood home to her and lifted the dark veil of torturing uncertainty from her mind.

On the day on which Lucia took her final vows, the other sisters in the Tuy convent learned to their great astonishment who was hidden in their midst under the name of Maria das Dores.

Lucia continued her quiet life in the convent, and was a

shining example to everyone. On the thirteenth of each month she returned in spirit to her native village and said the rosary with the thousands of pilgrims in the Cova da Iria.

The apparitions at Fatima had basically changed the whole life of Portugal. The godless regime in Lisbon had lost power. A Christian Government had been elected, and had restored the freedom of the Church. It was a great moment when General Carmona, the President, and Senhora Oliveira, the Premier, and many members of the Government went on pilgrimage to the Cova da Iria and paid homage to the Blessed Virgin.

When the red storm of revolution raged over Spain, churches, monasteries and convents went up in flames, and thousands of priests, religious and lay persons were martyred, Portugal remained immune from similar horrors. Jacinta's prayers had been heard.

Then, one icy-cold January night in the year 1938, the sign predicted by the Blessed Virgin appeared in the heavens: a flaming northern light appeared over all the countries of Europe. The Second World War, with its long succession of terrors, began, and soon enveloped half the world in flames, just as the little seer had seen in the vision at Valinhos. But again Portugal remained untouched by the conflagration.

In October, 1942, on the twenty-fifth anniversary of the Miracle of the Sun at Fatima, Pope Pius XII solemnly dedicated the whole world to the Immaculate Heart of Mary.

The great Message of Fatima, first kindled like a flame in the remote Cova da Iria, now spread all over the globe.

On the 13th of May, 1946, the Papal Legate, Cardinal Benedetto Aloisi-Masella, placed a precious crown on the statue of Our Lady of Fatima in the name of the Holy Father. On this occasion the Pope himself broadcast to the Portuguese nation and to the vast crowds from all parts of the world assembled in the Cova da Iria:

"You are crowning Mary not only as Queen of Portugal but as Queen of Peace and Queen of the World, because she will help the world to find peace and to rise again from its ruins."

Immense pilgrimages come from all parts of the world to Fatima. And the Blessed Virgin herself, represented by her statue from Fatima crowned with a golden crown, has toured the whole world bestowing blessings and graces on those who could not go themselves to the Cova da Iria to pay homage to her. Signs and wonders have accompanied this journey of Our Lady of Fatima in every part of the world.

Once upon a time three little children recited their rosary in that silent valley in Portugal. Now the number of those whose names are registered in the Golden Book of Fatima, and who have undertaken to recite the rosary daily with their families, has grown beyond all reckoning.

The white Basilica rises majestically above the place of the apparitions, pointing its golden dome toward heaven.

But Lucia's path has taken a still more silent course. On the 13th of May, 1948, the thirty-first anniversary of her first vision of Our Lady, she exchanged the habit of a Sister of St. Dorothy for that of a Carmelite nun, and entered the Convent of Our Lady of Carmel in Coimbra.

Some of the secrets which the Mother of God entrusted to her have been disclosed in accordance with God's will. Others still remain undisclosed, until the hour when they are to be revealed.

Oct. 30, 1934:   Lucia takes her final vows

Oct. 30, 1942:   Pope Pius XII dedicates the world to the Immaculate Heart of Mary

May 13, 1946:   Coronation of the statue of Our Lady of Fatima
Completion of the Basilica

May 13, 1947:   Start of the triumphal procession through the world of the statue of Our Lady of Fatima

May 13, 1948:   Lucia enters the Carmelite Convent in Coimbra